MUSHROOMS & TOADSTOOLS

AN ILLUSTRATED GUIDE

MUSHROOMS & TOADSTOOLS

AN ILLUSTRATED GUIDE

Text by Jiří Baier

Illustrations by Bohumil Vančura

Designed and produced by Aventinum Publishing House
Prague, Czech Republic

English language edition first published 1995
by Sunburst Books, Deacon House,
65 Old Church Street, London SW3 5BS

© AVENTINUM NAKLADATELSTVÍ, s. r. o., 1991

Text by Jiří Baier
Translated by Elizabeth Kindlová
Illustrations by Bohumil Vančura
Graphic design by Josef Dvořák

ISBN 1 85778 062 0
Printed in Slovakia
3/21/03/51-01

CONTENTS

Introduction

Mushrooms have been picked by people since the age of the hunter-gatherers, when they had to devise their own ways of distinguishing the edible from the poisonous mushrooms. Ancient rock paintings, dating as far back as the Stone Age, show humans' interest in and use of mushrooms. Some paintings on the Chukotskiy Peninsula, in the Bering Straits region, have shown human figures with pictures of mushrooms. There is speculation that they are the mushroom Fly Agaric, which was used in the drug Soma. This drug has been written about in old Indian sources, clarified by the famous ethnomycologist, R.G. Wasson. According to him, the Soma drug, derived from Fly Agaric, was prepared by priests as an intoxicating beverage with hallucinogenic effects, for religious or cult rituals. This theory is supported by the observation of indigenous groups on the Kamchatka Peninsula where the intoxicating effects of the Fly Agaric are still used in place of alcohol.

The French mycologist, R. Heim, has provided information about ancient cult uses of mushrooms from the region of present-day Mexico. The hallucinogenic effects of Psilocybe were used by the local witch doctors for predicting the future.

The first written references about mushrooms are found in the work of Aristotle's pupil, Theophrastus (372–287 B.C.), in which mushrooms are called 'mykes' and 'hydnom'. Even the Roman scholar, Pliny the Elder (23–79 A.D.), wrote about mushrooms and called them 'fungus', 'suillus' and 'boletus'. Ancient scholars wrote about the relationship between mushrooms and people, as well as trying to explain the complicated relationship between mushrooms and the plant kingdom. The mycorrhizal relationships between certain mushrooms and trees were described in the second half of the 19th century by B. Frank. For example, Pliny the Elder had already stated that most mushrooms grow in oak woods.

Documents on the culinary use of mushrooms are very scanty. It is known that the Roman Emperor Claudius was a great lover of mushrooms. The Roman poet, Martial (40–104 A.D.), known for his satirical epigrams, wrote about mushrooms: 'Easy it is to relinquish silver, gold, clothing and cloaks, but difficult it is to relinquish culinary mushroom delights'. Euripides, the Greek dramatist (c. 480–406 B.C.) lost his wife, daughter and two sons in one day, due to mushroom poisoning. Pope Clement VII, Roman Emperor Jovian, Charles VI and other rulers suffered a similar fate. In the Middle Ages, poisoning was a frequent method used to remove politically undesirable figures. Poisonous mushrooms were a particularly good method because there was no proof of evil intention.

In the countries of east Asia, in China, Japan and Burma, various edible mushrooms have been grown for thousands of years. In Europe, Pliny the Elder wrote: 'The bark of a white poplar scattered across manured furrows makes edible mushrooms grow throughout the year'. This was probably the method used in the ancient Roman Empire for the artificial cultivation of *Agrocybe aegerita*, the cultivation of which is currently being redeveloped.

The foundations of modern mycology were laid by Christian Hendrik Persoon (1755–

1837), a French botanist, in his publication *Synopsis methodica fungorum* (*Synopsis on the Methodology of Mushrooms*). His work was continued by Elias Magnus Fries (1794–1878), a Swedish botanist, who in his multi-volume work, *Systema mycologicum*, created the foundations of the scientific nomenclature of mushrooms. Since then, hundreds of mycological studies have been written. In recent years new disciplines have arisen, using mushrooms in biotechnologies. For example, mushrooms contain insoluble nitrogenous substances, which are thought to encourage peristalsis of the intestines, and absorb harmful metabolic products. Mushrooms also contain anti-allergic substances which can help conditions such as eczema, asthmatic bronchitis and allergic rash. Antitumorous activity has been discovered in some mushrooms, for example: the Velvet Shank, Oblique Inonotus, Birch Bracket, Oyster Fungus, Honey Fungus, Field Mushroom, Giant Puffball, and even the Penny Bun Bolete. Research on mushrooms continues to uncover more interesting facts.

Poisonous or not?

Poisonous mushrooms affect people and animals differently. Investigations continue to be carried out on the chemical analysis of mushrooms, and on their effect on the metabolism of various creatures.

Some animals are not affected by mushrooms that are poisonous to humans. The author did an experiment in which slugs were fed the poisonous mushroom, Death Cap, for two weeks. The slugs thrived and grew fat on a quantity of mushrooms which would have killed several human beings.

Whether a mushroom is poisonous to an animal depends on the metabolism of that animal. The primitive metabolism of the slug rendered the Death Cap harmless. Other poisonous mushrooms are host to worms. Some flies lay eggs in the flesh of poisonous mushrooms – when they hatch the larvae live off the mushrooms.

The mycologist, F. Guth, describes the poisoning of a cat which drank milk containing crushed Fly Agaric. After a few minutes the cat began vomiting, foaming at the mouth, was wide-eyed and its hind legs were paralysed. It recovered within three days and could walk properly in two weeks.

Laboratory tests have shown that herbivores suffer less effects from poisonous mushrooms than carnivores. The same quantity may cause little effect on a herbivore while the carnivore may die.

Poisonous mushrooms are therefore so-called because of their danger to people, for whom they are most dangerous. The term 'toadstool' is sometimes used to refer to poisonous or inedible mushrooms. An edible mushroom is never called a 'toadstool'.

Use of poisonous mushrooms

Throughout history, there have been cases of the use of poisonous mushrooms to remove enemies. According to Dr Robert Vávra, a renowned mycologist, the oldest known mushroom poisoning was the death of the Roman Emperor Claudius in 54 A.D. as described by Suetonius Tranquillus, the Roman historian. It is well known that mushrooms were considered a choice delicacy and were an essential part of the meals of Roman emperors. Caesar's Amanita was very popular, as recorded in the works of Pliny or Martial. Apicius, a well-known spendthrift and epicurean, committed suicide when he lost his fortune because he was afraid he would be unable to afford mushroom delicacies anymore.

Poisoning with mushrooms was not necessarily a simple matter. Emperor Claudius had his own taster, Halotus the eunuch. Most poisons took effect quickly during the tasting test, but if a mushroom such as Death Cap was used, the latency period would be long enough for the poison to reach the emperor. The art of poisoning in ancient Rome was quite refined though, and those who wished to commit murder had enough knowledge to do so.

Poisoning was easily carried out as the mushrooms could be disguised in broth or other dishes.

Mistaking or underestimating poisonous mushrooms

There have been cases where children have picked mushrooms and thoroughly cleaned them before taking them home. Their parents could then not distinguish the peeled poisonous mushrooms from edible ones and have unfortunately cooked them for supper.

Most people who have picked poisonous mushrooms have been convinced they were picking good edible mushrooms. The Death Cap in particular has often been mistaken and has caused many an unfortunate death.

One case written about is that of a mother who often picked champignons around Prague. One day, apart from edible mushrooms, she also picked ten Death Caps, thinking they were Wood Mushrooms which have a greenish cap if the sun does not reach them. She made a mushroom omelette that evening. The following morning her whole family were ill with diarrhoea and vomiting and were completely exhausted. Despite quick hospital treatment the whole family died within the following two weeks, the children dying first.

It is very dangerous to try and identify an unknown species by yourself. The beauty of a mushroom is no indication of whether it is edible. Tasting a little and waiting to see the effect is not a good idea, particularly as some poisonous mushrooms have a long latency period – that is, it can take many many hours, even days, for the poison to take effect.

Raw mushrooms should also not be tasted in the forest while picking, in spite of the recommendations of some keen pickers. It is fine to do this with russulas or when wishing to distinguish the Bitter Boletus from Penny Bun Bolete or the Tufted Yellow Agaric/Conifer from the Sulphur Tuft. However, even in such cases it is not recommended to swallow the mushroom being tasted. If the Devil's Boletus is accidentally mistaken for one of the coloured boletes, then even a small bit of this raw mushroom could cause poisoning and considerable health problems.

The toxins of poisonous mushrooms from food may reach the milk of breast-feeding mothers. In view of the small weight of a baby, even a mild poisoning of the mother could prove fatal for the baby. So breast-feeding mothers should avoid mushrooms of whose identity there is the slightest doubt.

Even mycologists have brought the danger of poisoning into their homes. After bringing unknown species into the house, someone else may think the mushroom is edible and use it for cooking, often resulting in poisoning.

Poisonous substances may get into preserved mushrooms. Never dry unknown or suspicious-looking mushrooms – they will be very difficult to identify later on. This is even more so with mushroom powder. So, only conserve mushrooms that you have no doubt about whatsoever.

Also, by not applying the correct technology or during the slow drying of certain species poisonous substances sometimes appear in dried mushrooms. For example, when drying the Red-Cracked/Cracked-Cap Bolete (*Xerocomus chrysenteron*), the parasitic lower *Apiocrea chrysosperma* may breed on the surface of its cap. Such parasites can cause illness. If you have no favourable conditions to dry mushrooms within 24 hours, then conserve them in a different way.

Superstitions

There are many age-old superstitions about determining whether or not a mushroom is poisonous. One of the most common states: 'a poisonous mushroom stings the mouth and has an unpleasant taste'. However, this is not true. The raw Spruce Milk Cap has a very unpleasant, even disgusting taste, but when cooked is one of the most delicious mushrooms. The same can be said of the Grass-Green/Green Russula, the Chanterelle and other mushrooms. The sting or bitterness of a mushroom may make it inedible but it is not necessarily poisonous. Many poisonous species in fact have a dull or even pleasant taste and smell. The most poisonous mushrooms neither burn nor are they bitter and they do not smell or stink. The highly poisonous Death Cap only has a slight smell after being cooked and is delicious when tasted.

Another false belief maintains that silver or silver-plated objects turn black when they touch a poisonous mushroom. This darkening does not indicate the presence of a toxin. Also, colour change in the flesh of a cut up fruit body is not a sign of poison. Boletes which turn blue are usually very tasty mushrooms, although poisonous species do also exist. The colour change results from the oxidising reaction of the pigment found in the mushroom and has got nothing to do with the toxins.

Another superstition claims that mushrooms nibbled by animals or resident larvae (wormy mushrooms) are edible. However, slugs or insects have a different metabolism and are not affected by the same toxins as humans.

Following superstitions is dangerous. No simple and common rule exists for recognising a poisonous mushroom. There is no other choice but to learn to distinguish mushrooms according to their botanical characteristics.

Types of poison and their symptoms

Poisonous mushrooms differ in the kind of toxin they contain and therefore cause different symptoms or health problems.

Many doctors, biochemists and mycologists throughout the world have researched mushroom poisoning and the various health problems caused by mushrooms. In this book, the classification of mushroom poisoning is based on the work of Czech doctors – toxicologists, Dr Josef Herink, Dr Jiří Kubička and Dr Jaroslav Veselský, who have become the founders of a new methodology for treating so-called phalloidine poisons.

According to their action on the individual organs of the human body, mushroom poisons can be divided into several basic categories:

1. Phalloidine poisons, which damage the liver, named after the Death Cap (*Amanita phalloides*). Mushrooms containing these include some small-coloured parasol mushrooms, some galerinas, the Gyromitra, the Sulphur Tuft and, above all, the Death Cap, the Fool's Mushroom/White Death Cap and Poisonous Amanita.

Mushrooms of the Death Cap order contain two types of highly concentrated poisonous substances called amatoxins and phallotoxins. These substances are among the most deadly of mushroom poisons. Up to 95% of people who eat these mushrooms die. The toxins quickly penetrate and damage liver cells.

The first symptoms of phalloidine poisoning only appear after a relatively long period – anything from six to 12 hours after consumption. The first symptoms are vomiting and diarrhoea, which last about two days. Heavy diarrhoea and vomiting cause a great loss of liquids and salt, which results in exhaustion and muscle cramps. The patient has trouble urinating or stops entirely, causing further problems. Enzymes called transaminases increase in concentration in the blood, as does the level of biliary pigments. The next stage of poisoning shows an apparent relief of the symptoms. If the patient is not treated quickly or has eaten a large amount of poisonous mushrooms, then the third stage of poisoning follows. The patient becomes unconscious and dies within six to eight days with liver failure. His skin shows signs of yellow jaundice.

Paraphalloidine poisonings occur after the consumption of mushrooms which do not contain poisons typical of the Death Cap, for example, the poisoning occurring after the consumption of the Gyromitra/False Morel/Brain Mushroom. After a longer latency period (five to ten hours), the patient begins to feel discomfort, gets a headache and stomach ache and keeps vomiting, although this does not last as long as in Death Cap poisoning. Diarrhoea is also not as common. It is relatively common that blood circulation ceases, leading to swelling of the brain. Yellow jaundice also appears in various intensity and poisoning sometimes ends with death in a liver failure-induced coma.

2. Orellanin poisoning affects the kidneys, named after Plush Cortinarius (*Cortinarius orellanus*). Other species of the Cortinarius group are also poisonous. The latency period is about two to three days in heavier cases of poisoning (after consumption of a fatal dose, i.e. 30 g of raw mushrooms), in moderately strong poisoning four to nine days and ten to seventeen days in milder cases of poisoning. It is difficult to determine the start of poisoning with repeated consumption of mushrooms because the toxin collects in the body. Increase in frequency of urination in the first stage of poisoning is also easily overlooked. The patient may only become aware of the poisoning when vomiting and diarrhoea, dryness in the mouth and thirst all set in. The excretion of urine gradually decreases and can stop altogether. However, thirst continues to increase – the patient may drink up to 10 litres a day. Pains begin in the stomache, kidney area and the joints. Sometimes the patient shivers but has no temperature. Later nervous symptoms, tiredness, twitching and shivering of the muscles, swelling of the lower limbs and eyelids all appear. The poisoning may take on a more rapid course in children, with death occurring within several days. In older people with damaged kidneys the course of poisoning is more deadly and more rapid. Convalescence lasts longer and sometimes the poisoning causes permanent kidney damage. Treatment is possible only in special departments of large hospitals equipped with haemodialysis of the blood, where the effects can be clearly monitored, and a kidney machine used. Chronic kidney damage may occur with the patient becoming permanently dependent on a kidney machine.

3. Muscarine poisoning, named after the Fly Agaric (*Amanita muscaria*), affects the digestive tract, nervous system, heart, sight and breathing. This poisoning occurs from the Fly Agaric, various inocybes, clitocybes, the Poison Pie, the Jack-O-Lantern and Rose Mycena. The latency period is very short. Sometimes symptoms already appear during the meal but usually within two hours after it. Symptoms include sweating profusely, salivation and teary eyes. Stomach discomfort begins with vomiting and diarrhoea, resulting in dehydration and sometimes cramps in the legs. The peripheral vessels expand, blood pressure drops, the pulse slows down, and the patient feels cold and shivers. The pupils narrow substantially, leading to disturbed vision. Breathing becomes difficult and can eventually stop altogether. Poisoning can prove fatal if not treated immediately.

4. Psychotropic poisoning affects brain tissue, causing psychic disturbances. It is caused by two types of poison – mycoatropine and psilocybine.

Mycoatropine poisoning is mainly caused by the *Amanita* species. Poisoning symptoms appear within a half an hour to three hours with nausea, vomiting, headache, heart palpitations and dilated pupils causing disturbed vision. Frequently a state resembling alcoholic intoxication results whereby the victim talks a lot, laughs or cries for no reason, hits himself, runs about and sometimes violently attacks someone. After this strong excitement, a fainting fit sets in whereby the patient wakes occasionally and has hallucinations, shouts, and defends himself against an invisible danger. Finally he falls into a deep sleep and usually wakes up feeling normal on the second or third day. The victim never remembers anything. This poisoning is particularly dangerous for older people with hardened arteries in the brain, or for people with heart problems.

The hallucinogenic poisoning caused by psilocybine, results from certain species of *Psilocybes, Panaeolus* and *Stropharia*.

Poisoning symptoms appear including blood vessel dilation, an alternating feeling of hot and cold and dilation of the pupils, accompanied by disturbed vision and hallucinations. The psychic symptoms of poisoning vary. Some patients experience a state of euphoria and laugh a lot. They experience defects in the colour of their vision, and a kaleidoscopic effect can result, with double vision. Others feel anxiety and fear, and have frightening visions leading to a state of delirium and suicide attempts. Poisoning symptoms last for several hours but have no lasting effect on healthy people.

5. Poisoning affecting the digestive tract is caused by the Tiger Tricholoma, Shingled Tricholoma, Leaden Entoloma, Springtime Nolanea, Yellow-Staining Agaricus, Yellowish Milk Cap, Bearded/Woolly Milk Cap, Earth Balls, stinging Russulas and Coral Fungi. Poisoning symptoms appear relatively quickly, in one to four hours after consumption.

Two big fruit bodies of the Tiger Tricholoma are enough to cause poisoning, the symptoms of which appear in half an hour to two hours with vomiting and diarrhoea. Apart from loss of liquids and salt, kidney damage can result. Several cases of death have also been reported.

Poisoning symptoms caused by the Shingled Tricholoma appear within two hours with discomfort and an urge to vomit. The patient cannot hold down any food. He vomits about 15 times but there is no relief. Painful abdominal cramps begin, as well as repeated diarrhoea. Sometimes there are defects in blood circulation and fainting fits accompanied by cold sweat, increased heart activity and symptoms caused by loss of liquids. This secondary state with feeling of exhaustion and bodily weakness may last several weeks.

Symptoms of poisoning by the Leaden Entoloma appear in two to four hours with strong diarrhoea and vomiting. This may last several days and results in considerable exhaustion. Sometimes the kidneys are also damaged. Older people may die from heart failure. Deaths due to poisoning by the Leaden Entoloma are known throughout central and southern Europe.

Symptoms of poisoning by the Springtime Nolanea appear in two to four hours (sometimes in 24 hours) with repeated diarrhoea, which lasts several days and results in considerable dehydration and exhaustion. Vomiting occurs in exceptional cases.

Symptoms of poisoning by the Yellow-Staining Agaricus begin in one to three hours after the meal if large amounts of mushrooms are eaten. There is vomiting which lasts for several hours, and diarrhoea in exceptional cases. The Flat-Top Agaricus causes a similar poisoning.

The Common Earth Ball causes poisoning with symptoms appearing in one to two hours resulting in persistent vomiting and diarrhoea. The patient complains of pressure on the stomach, which changes into a dull pain. The central nervous system is affected, causing buzzing in the ears, headache, a feeling of intoxication and drowsiness. There may also be feelings of heat, dizziness and uncertainty, sweating and difficulty in breathing through the nose. The symptoms fade away after several hours.

After eating certain stinging Russulas and Milk Caps, poisoning results in one to four hours with repeated diarrhoea and vomiting, but it does not last long.

Coral Fungi contains the laxative substance called emodin which strongly irritates the mucous membrane of the large intestine. Poisoning by Coral Fungi is not dangerous but very unpleasant due to incessant diarrhoea.

6. Certain mushrooms mixed with alcohol result in digestive, heart and psychic problems. This type of poisoning is associated with the Antabuse Ink Cap or with the Glistening Ink Cap. The Antabuse Ink Cap is edible and very tasty. However, if the mushroom is eaten while drinking an alcoholic beverage, then the effects of coprin set in, blocking the activity of enzymes in the liver. Acetaldehyde poisoning appears within 30 minutes with a conspicuous reddening of the face spreading to the body and upper limbs. Further symptoms include heart palpitations, breathlessness, diarrhoea and fear of dying. The symptoms are very unpleasant and directly proportional to the amount of mushrooms and alcohol consumed. They fade away in two to three hours but if further alcohol is consumed then the poisoning could return (up to the fourth day after consumption of the mushrooms).

First aid for mushroom poisoning

Discomfort after the consumption of a mushroom dish does not necessarily mean poisoning. This can be caused by eating too many mushrooms. Mushrooms are particularly hard to digest when eaten with eggs, semolina or a large amount of fat. The more serious the health problems and the longer the time they take to appear after a meal, the more dangerous the poisoning. The longer latency period is typical for poisoning by the Death Cap.

If you suspect mushroom poisoning then it is most essential to:

a) Call a doctor immediately or take the person to the nearest hospital, regardless of what time it is.

b) Inform the doctor that the person has eaten mushrooms.

c) Find the rest of any unprepared or uneaten mushrooms as well as any bits of mushroom in the vomit or the faeces and give this to the hospital staff. Correct and effective medical aid depends considerably on the quick and reliable determination of the species of mushroom consumed.

Before the doctor arrives you could do the following:

a) Try to make the patient vomit as quickly and as much as possible. Sometimes this happens on its own, but it is with the most poisonous species of the Death Cap group that vomiting does not take place until later on. In order to encourage vomiting, give the patient warm and slightly salted water. Keep up the vomiting until the food with the mushrooms comes up in the vomit.

b) Do not give the patient any food. Only give him plain water, or water with lemon and sugar. Do not give milk or any alcohol as this will worsen the course of the poisoning.

c) If it is at all possible in between the vomiting and diarrhoea, get the patient to stay in bed.

d) Only medicinal charcoal from the first-aid box may be given to the victim with a dosage of 20 tablets at once. Keen mushroom pickers should keep an ample supply of medicinal charcoal.

It is important to follow these suggested measures. About 10 to 15% of people poisoned by mushrooms die. The toxic effect of mushrooms is underestimated so that specialised treatment comes too late. Effective treatment procedures can dramatically reduce the mortality rate, with the commencement of intensive treatment in the first 36 hours after consumption.

The biology of fungi

Mycology, the study of fungi, is a relatively young science. Research into mycoflora is far from complete. The total number of species of fungi is estimated at 80 to 100 thousand and new species are still being discovered. Most of them consist of microscopic fungi whose bodies are not divided into a mycelium and a true fruit body. These include moulds and yeast plants essential for the food industry, as well as fungi which cause plant, animal and human diseases; destroy fruit, vegetables, bread, wood and textiles. On our planet there are 15 to 20 thousand species of higher and bigger mushrooms, which are called macromycetes.

Five to six thousand species grow in Europe alone. Six to eight of these species are deadly poisonous; about 100 species are poisonous or health-threatening. About 500 species are edible, though only about 100 of these species are very tasty. The rest are inedible, have not yet been tested, or are rare.

The classification of mushrooms into edible, inedible and poisonous is highly problematical. The toxicity of mushrooms is relative up to a certain degree. Roger Henry, a French mycologist, correctly said: 'Edible mushrooms are those that are least poisonous'. Dangerous poisonous substances are found, in varying

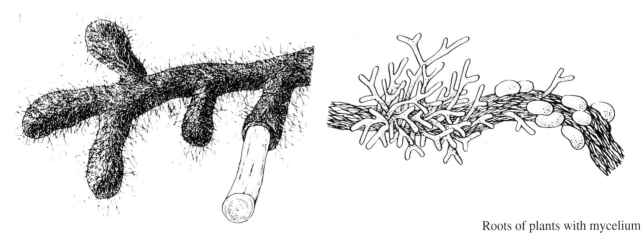

Roots of plants with mycelium

15

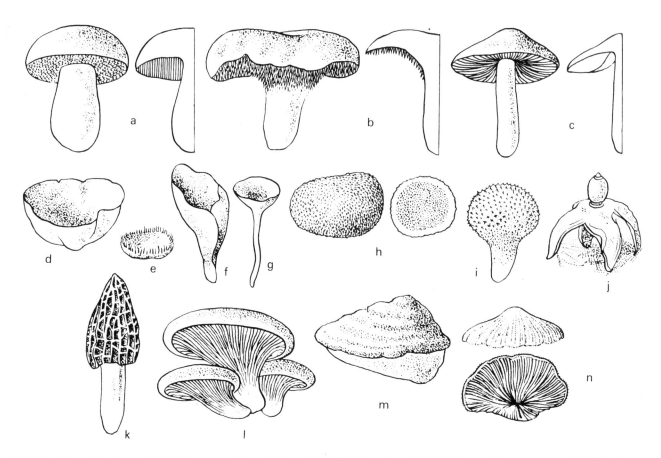

Fruit bodies: a) boletes, b) Hydnaceae, c) Agaricales, d) e) f) g) various fruit bodies of Ascomycetes, h) *Elaphomyces*, i) Lycoperdales, j) *Geastrum*, k) Morchellaceae, l) *Pleurotus*, m) polypores, n) *Schizophyllum*

amounts, in boletes or other confirmed species. The term poisonous mushroom has not been precisely defined as yet. Hence edible mushrooms are those species regarded as not capable of poisoning if used in appropriate amounts and cooked or prepared and processed properly.

Inedible mushrooms are regarded as being species which, for various reasons, are unusable because they are, for example, too tough, strong, bitter or sour. It is also relative whether mushrooms can be used or not. In some places, traditional methods may exist which can transform an unusable or even poisonous species into a delicacy. Of course, such a cooking method has to be tried and tested using the correct species of mushroom.

Although there are relatively few actually

poisonous and health-threatening mushrooms, you should never take a risk when picking them for cooking purposes.

Poisonous mushrooms can only be distinguished from edible ones by a perfect knowledge of their biological characteristics. If a mushroom cannot be determined precisely then it should not be consumed. If in doubt, don't!

Only specialist mycologists are likely to identify mushrooms with inconspicuous characteristics.

Mushrooms are thalloid plants without green-plant pigment (chlorophyll), no transport vessels and are therefore totally different in their method of nutrition to green plants. Being unable to produce energy through photosynthesis, as green plants do, fungi acquire their organic matter and energy from the decomposition of dead or live matter of other organisms. This method of getting nourishment is called heterotrophic. Fungi play an important role as decomposers of various waste products of the metabolism of other organisms.

Fungi have been found in Palaeozoic fossils of horsetails. Polypores have been found in coal dating from the Mesozoic age and Tertiary period whose firmly erect fruit bodies enabled their fossilisation. There are at least 500 species of fossilised mushrooms, but there must be many more unknown species, as soft fruit bodies were not preserved.

In accordance with their way of life, mushrooms are divided into three basic categories: 1. Symbiotic fungi (mycorrhizal fungi), 2. Fungi subsisting on dead or decaying matter (saprophytic fungi), 3. Fungi feeding on living organisms (parasitic fungi).

Symbiotic fungi contain the most interesting species of mushrooms growing in the forest. The fibres of their mycelium wind around or penetrate the roots of higher vascular plants –
mostly trees, bushes and forest grasses. The fungus partially substitutes for the root systems of trees. It takes necessary substances from the tree, mostly sugar, and in return provides the tree with important substances for its life and growth which it takes from the soil and air. This mycorrhizal relationship is successful for both partners, and trees where the relationship is perfectly developed, receive a better supply of nutrients and grow better. If, however, the fungus disappears due to unsuitable external conditions, the tree usually dies.

Many species of fungi live in a mycorrhizal relationship with plants. Some have a close relationship with only one tree, e.g. the Tamarack Jack with the larch, the Olive-Brown Wax Cap (*Hygrophorus hypothejus*) with the pine or the Birch Bolete with the birch. Elsewhere a fungus does not have a specific host and many grow next to various trees. Most boletes, russulas, tricholomas, amanitas and tuberales belong to this category. The close relationship between the mushroom and forest woody plant is interesting. In some countries attempts have been made to inject mycorrhizal fungi onto forest saplings. A greater percentage

Cap: a) convex, low-arched, b) flat, c) with blunt knob, d) with pointed papilla, e) depressed, f) funnel-shaped, g) bell-shaped, h) bell-shaped, grooved with sharp knob, i) section of lateral growing cap, j) section of semi-developed cap

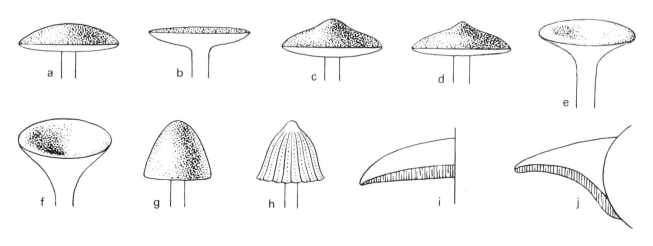

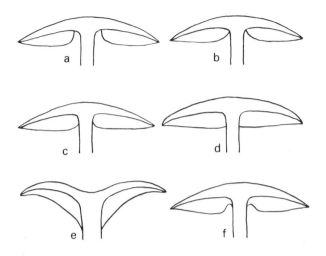

Attachment of the gills to the stem:
a) gills free (not attached), b) gills loose, c) gills adnexed, narrowly attached, d) gills adnate (broadly attached), e) gills decurrent (running down the stem), f) gills sinuate (notched)

of rooted trees and thicker growth was achieved. The same principle is used to cultivate certain species of good mushrooms, suitable for culinary purposes.

Saprophytic fungi drain nutrition from dead bodies of plants and animals, at various stages of their decay. With the aid of special enzymes, the mushrooms are able to decompose organic matter into nutrients and energy. This category includes such mushrooms as champignons, Morchellaceae, *Hypholoma*, *Pholiota*, *Kuehneromyces*, certain Gasteromycetes and other species. People have artifically cultivated these mushrooms to decompose matter, especially in east Asian countries.

Parasitic species belong to the third category and these may attack living trees, cultured crops and people, causing great losses in food and other products. Examples include: *Claviceps*, wheat rust, the Honey Fungus, various polypores and finally species which can cause unpleasant skin diseases.

The fruit bodies of picked mushrooms are their reproductive organs. The actual mushroom body consists of hyphae fibres which form the mycelium. Both the mycelium and the fruit body can be used to determine the species of mushroom. The individual families

and species of mushrooms are distinguished according to their macroscopic and microscopic characteristics. In this book only the macroscopic characteristics are described, which are those visible to the naked eye.

The fruit bodies of individual species differ in size, shape and consistency, smell, taste and colouring of the flesh. The flesh is a very important characteristic for determining the species of a mushroom. It may be fibrous, watery, juicy, dry or woody. When cut, its colour may change. Sometimes it releases liquid and its colouring changes when it comes into contact with air.

An important part of the fruit body is the cap or pileus. This too may have its characteristic shape: convex, flat, bell-shaped, funnel-shaped. There are gills or tubes on the underside of the cap which are covered with a hymenium. Spores form on the hymenium. These hymenomycetes mushrooms may be various shapes such as gilled, tubed, bristly.

In gilled mushrooms it is very important to know how the gills are attached to the stem: decurrent, running down the stem; free, not attached.

Another part of the fruit body is the stem (or stipe), the end of which is important. It may be rounded off, blunt-ended, pointed, bulbous, bulbous with a volva, root-shaped, narrowed off. The surface of the stem may be smooth, grooved, wrinkled, ridged, naked, scaly, viscid, differently coloured. A ring (or annulus) forms on the stem of certain mushrooms which appears from the veil covering the young gills. The drawing below shows how a ring, or volva, appears.

Another macroscopic characteristic is the colour of the spores. In order to find this out, let the spores fall out of the fruit body onto some white paper and cover with a glass. In several hours a continuous layer will appear on the paper of spore dust which – for example in gilled mushrooms – forms the exact shape of the gills. The colour of the spore dust is characteristic of a certain family.

The picture section of this book depicts and describes not only poisonous or health-threatening mushrooms, but also similar edible species which they are often confused with. To avoid repeating the same description of certain edible mushrooms, clear page references are given.

Appearance of the ring:
a) on the Death Cap, b) on agarics, c) on Cortinariaceae (no membranous ring forms on Cortinariaceae, but a russet-coloured band with fixed fibres remains after the veil disappears).

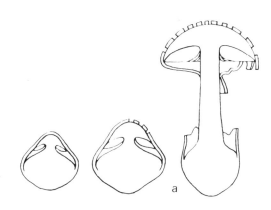 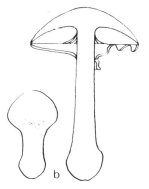 

An illustrated comparison of poisonous and edible mushrooms

☠ Gyromitra; False Morel; Brain Mushroom

Gyromitra esculenta (Pers. ex Pers.) Fr.

The cap is 30 to 120 mm wide and high, irregularly spherical, with brainlike folds, hollow, chestnut to dark-brown and growing darker (even turning black) with age. The stem is cylindrical, hollow, with pits on the surface, whitish, even slightly reddish, 20 to 60 mm high, 15 to 30 mm wide. The flesh is thin, whitish, watery, of no distinctive taste and has a mild mushroom smell. The spores are ellipsoid, smooth, colourless with two small oil drops at the poles and measure 18-22 x 8-12 μm. It grows from April to June in coniferous woodlands mostly beneath pine trees, most often on sandy soils, but it can also be found on stumps, woodland paths and borders. In some places it is abundant, elsewhere it does not grow at all. Formerly it was considered to be an edible mushroom, picked and sold at markets. However, occasionally poisoning symptoms appeared when the mushroom was consumed, particularly in June. In medical literature several cases of death after the consumption of this species have been recorded, therefore it is listed under poisonous mushrooms and not recommended for cooking purposes. Of the springtime Helvellaceae, only the mushroom known as the Snow Mushroom/Snowbank False Morel/Bull Nose/Walnut can be safely recommended, whose edibility has been fully tested and approved.

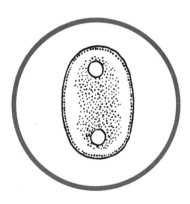

The microscopic examination of ripened spores can distinguish the Gyromitra/False Morel/Brain Mushroom from the Snow Mushroom/Snowbank False Morel/Bull Nose/Walnut.

Snow Mushroom; Snowbank False Morel; Bull Nose; Walnut

Neogyromitra gigas (Krombh.) Imai

Morchellaceae

Conical Morel

Morchella conica Pers.

Snow Mushroom; Snowbank False Morel; Bull Nose; Walnut

The cap is irregularly spherical, partly lobed, hollow, and brainlike or with twisted folds. The base of the cap is attached to the stem, tan, olive brown or lightbrown to brown in colour, 60 to 150 mm wide. The stem is very short, thick, hollow, irregularly pitted, depressed, whitish, dirty-white to tan in colour. The flesh is whitish or light-greyish, thin and fragile, with no distinctive taste and smell. It grows from April to May in warm deciduous or mixed woodlands of highly decomposed wood. It can be found on rotting stumps of spruce trees or on fallen trunks of ash trees, aspens or other deciduous trees. It differs from the Gyromitra/False Morel/Brain Mushroom in its spores which are smooth, colourless, elongated ellipsoids with papilla-like appendices on the ends, and with two smaller drops at the poles and one bigger one in the middle, 28-38 x 12-14 µm in size.

Conical Morel

The cap is up to 80 mm high, funnel-shaped, brown-grey to black-grey in colour, hollow with prominent lengthwise parallel ridges, diagonally linked and defined oblong pits. It grows in spring on woodland borders found on higher ground. It differs from the Gyromitra/False Morel/Brain Mushroom mainly due to the small depressions on the surface of its cap.

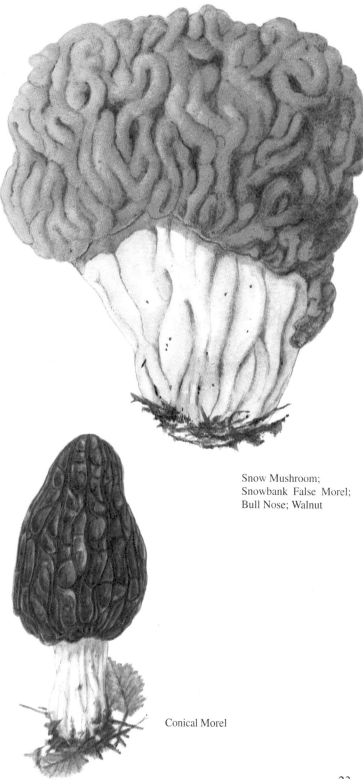

Snow Mushroom; Snowbank False Morel; Bull Nose; Walnut

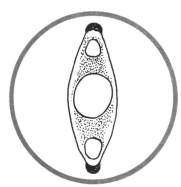

The Snow Mushroom/Snowbank False Morel/Bull Nose/ Walnut has elongated ellipsoid spores with papilla-like appendices on the ends, two smaller drops at the poles and one bigger one in the middle.

Conical Morel

☠ Gyromitra; False Morel; Brain Mushroom – white form

Gyromitra esculenta var. *alba* Pilát

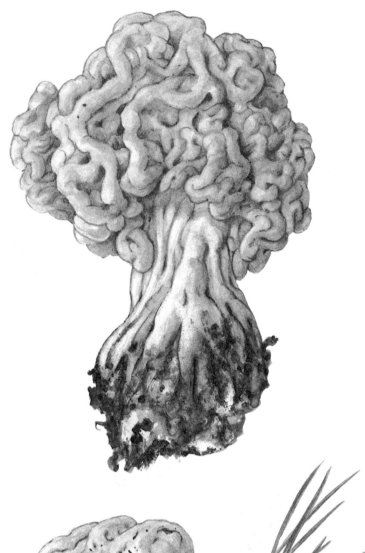

The cap is irregularly spherical with brainlike folds, hollow, grows to 50 mm in size, whitish to light creamy-ochre; when dried it turns brown in the depressed parts. The stem is pure white, cylindrical with coarse grooves or irregular pits on the surface, flaky papilla-like on the upper part inside with irregular hollows mainly in the lower part. The flesh is thin, white, watery with no distinctive taste and a slight mushroom smell. It grows quite rarely in April and May in coniferous woodlands. It is mainly found under pine trees growing on sandy ground. No evidence exists as yet about the toxicity of this white form, but it is most probably just as dangerous as the Gyromitra/False Morel/Brain Mushroom. It is therefore not recommended for cooking purposes although some experts claim that blanching removes poisonous substances from the mushroom. The white form of the Gyromitra/False Morel/Brain Mushroom can be confused with the spring species of the lighter young fruit bodies of the Common Morel or the young Wrinkled Thimble Morel.

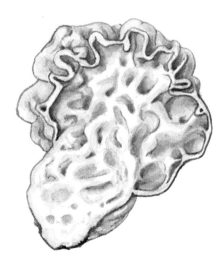

A section of the fruit body of the white form of the Gyromitra/False Morel/Brain Mushroom

Common Morel 🍴

Morchella esculenta (L.) ex St. Am.

Wrinkled Thimble Morel 🍴

Ptychoverpa bohemica (Krombh.) Schroet.

Common Morel

The cap measures 40 to 90 mm, is spherical or egg-shaped, hollow with a criss-crossed irregular network of ridges which divide the hollows, with a matt, ochre to tan surface. The stem is cylindrical, hollow, white and is adherent to the base of the cap while the lower part is broader. The flesh is thin, gristly, fragile, whitish, indistinctive, but with a pleasant taste and smell. It grows in relative abundance from April to May in groves, orchards and gardens. It is edible. It differs from Gyromitras/False Morels/Brain Mushrooms as it has hollows on the surface of the cap (Gyromitras/False Morels/Brain Mushrooms have brainlike folds on their surface).

Wrinkled Thimble Morel

The cap is bell-shaped, up to 40 mm high, thin-fleshed, ochre in colour when young, and attached to the stem at the apex by a small area. The small cylindrical stem is often concealed under the cap and only several millimetres of it are visible. In old age the cap grows dark-brown with lengthwise lobed ridges; the stem grows up to 30 mm in length. The flesh is whitish with a very pleasant mushroom taste and smell. It grows from March to May in warmer deciduous groves under ash trees, aspens, cherry and rowan trees. It is edible and is one of the tastiest of mushrooms. It can be distinguished from Gyromitras/False Morels/ Brain Mushrooms by a cross-section of the fruit body whereby the stem is attached to the cap.

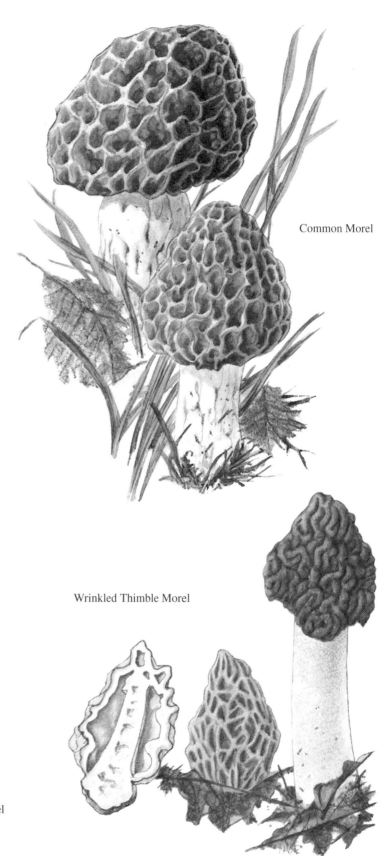

Common Morel

Wrinkled Thimble Morel

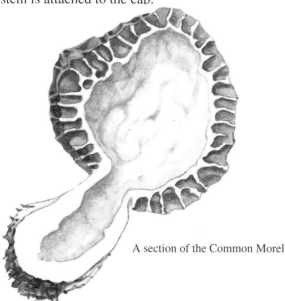

A section of the Common Morel

☠ Springtime Morel; Pointed Gyromitra

Neogyromitra fastigiata (Krombh.)

The cap has a brown or olive-brown surface, is hollow and saddle-shaped with veined folds usually ending in two to three lobed ends; the underside is attached to the stem and it is 60 to 120 mm wide. The stem is whitish, thickly wrinkled (sort of pointed), rimy, 30 to 60 mm wide, and brownish at the base. The flesh is whitish or light-greyish, thin, fragile with an indistinctive taste and smell. It grows in April and May in deciduous woodlands on limestone ground mostly under hornbeams, oaks and linden trees. It prefers warmer sites. It is not too abundant in growth. It may cause poisoning but its poisonous substances have not been identified as yet. The harmful substances are more concentrated if the mushrooms are left to grow for a long time. The Springtime Morel/Pointed Gyomitra should definitely not be picked for culinary use.

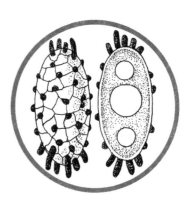

The spores of the Springtime Morel/Pointed Gyromitra

Snow Mushroom; Snowbank False Morel; Bull Nose; Walnut

Neogyromitra gigas (Krombh.) Imai

A detailed description of the Snow Mushroom/Snowbank False Morel/Bull Nose/Walnut is given on page 23. This edible and tasty mushroom grows, but not in great abundance, from April to May in warm deciduous and mixed woodlands with decaying wood. It is found both in lowlands and on foothills. It is favoured by mushroom pickers as it grows early in the season when few edible mushrooms appear. It is mostly used for cooking soups and sauces. It has the best taste when dried (e.g. poultry cooked in dried Snow Mushrooms is highly recommended). It can be distinguished from the dangerous Springtime Morel/Pointed Gyomitra by a microscopic examination of well-ripened fruit bodies. The spores of the Snow Mushroom/Snowbank False Morel/Bull Nose/Walnut are elongated ellipsoids with papilla-like appendices on the ends, smooth, colourless with two smaller drops at the poles and one bigger one in the middle, 28-32 x 12-14 µm; the ripened spores of the Springtime Morel/Pointed Gyromitra have an ornamental mesh consisting of papilla-like to bristly outgrowths.

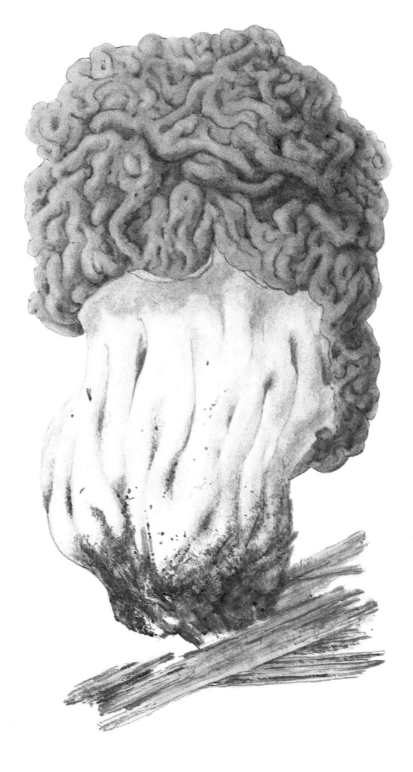

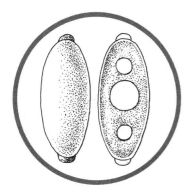

The spores of the Snow Mushroom/Snowbank False Morel/Bull Nose/Walnut

Springtime Nolanea

Nolanea verna (Lund.) Kotl. et Pouz.

The cap is 30 to 60 mm wide; conical when young with a prominent knob soon becoming flat and folded; thin-fleshed; in damp weather brown, brown-red to black-grey; in dry weather grey-brown with a silky shine. The gills are sparse, high, sinuate at the stem, fragile, grey-ochre when young and pink once the spores ripen. The stem is cylindrical, slender, often twisted into a figure eight with a lengthwise groove, hollow, fragile, brittle, white and tomentose at the base, grey-brown. The flesh is grey-white, with a slightly floury taste and indistinctive smell. It grows abundantly from April to June on pastureland, boundaries, in groves and light woodlands either individually or in clumps. It never grows in rings like the Fairy-Ring Champignon, with which it is often confused. It is sometimes mistaken by mushroom pickers for the Cone Collybia because both grow in the same season. The cap of the Springtime Nolanea, though it resembles the cap of the Fairy-Ring Champignon, is far more fragile, has thicker pinkish gills and a different smell. It is a slightly poisonous mushroom.

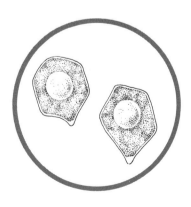

The spores of the Springtime Nolanea

Fairy-Ring Champignon

Marasmius oreades (Bolt. ex Fr.) Fr.

Cone Collybia

Strobilurus esculentus (Wulf. ex Fr.) Sing.

Fairy-Ring Champignon

A detailed description of the Fairy-Ring Champignon is given on pages 33 and 73. It differs from the Springtime Nolanea in its flexible stem flesh, very sparse gills, bitter almond smell and smooth ellipsoid spores that are 7-9 x 4-5 µm in size; the Springtime Nolanea has angular spores that are pink, 8-11 x 7-8 µm in size.

Cone Collybia

The cap grows to 15 to 25 mm in size, is thin-fleshed, arched when young and later flat, light brown-grey to dark brown and completely smooth. The gills are thin, whitish at first and later greyish in colour. The stem is thin, long, smooth, fibrillose beneath the ground and light ochre. The flesh is very thin, whitish, with a pleasant taste and a delicious mushroom smell. It grows mostly in early spring, particularly in damp spruce woods from lowlands to mountain areas. It grows on rotting cones buried in the ground. It is one of the tasty edible mushrooms. On the grassy borders of spruce woods it is sometimes mistaken by mushroom pickers for the Springtime Nolanea because both grow in the same season. They can be easily distinguished by their spores – the Springtime Nolanea has angular pink ones while the Cone Collybia has smooth colourless ellipsoids. The older fruit bodies of the Springtime Nolanea can be identified by the thickness and colour of the gills.

Fairy-Ring Champignon

The spores and cystidia of the Cone Collybia

Cone Collybia

☠ Blushing Inocybe

Cortinariaceae

Inocybe erubescens Blytt.

The cap is 30 to 100 mm wide, egg-shaped when young but soon becoming bell-shaped, often folded, later flat with a flat margin and a distinctive knob on the apex, radially cracked. The skin is whitish when young, with a silky shine. When older, or if creased, vermilion spots and cracks appear. The gills are sinuate, thick, whitish at first but soon becoming olive-grey then dark ochre with reddish spots, white and flaky on the edges. The stem is cylindrical, firm, full, white at first then red-spotted to completely red-brown in colour and with lengthwise fibres. The flesh is white, becoming reddish where cut, with a slight taste and a mellow fruit smell. It grows from May to July in parks, gardens, in deciduous woodlands under isolated deciduous trees especially under lindens, oaks, beeches and hornbeams. It prefers warmer sites with limestone ground. In favourable conditions it grows in large clumps. It is a highly poisonous mushroom, containing five times more muscarine poison than the Fly Agaric. A fatal dose is 100 to 500 g of fresh mushrooms. Poisoning symptoms appear soon after consumption with salivation, heart palpitations, discomfort in the heart region and eventually the slowing down of heart activity. The victim dies without immediate medical treatment, but a dose of atropine can usually save his life. The Blushing Inocybe is often confused with the St. George's Mushroom because both species grow in spring and may be found in the same areas.

The young fruit body of the Blushing Inocybe

St. George's Mushroom
Calocybe gambosa (Fr.) Donk

The cap is 30 to 100 mm wide, almost convex at first, later bell-shaped, soon becoming widely arched with a long, rounded and inrolled margin, whitish to ochre, rarely yellowish, smooth, naked with thick flesh. The gills are very dense, conspicuously low, sinuate and decurrent at the stem, whitish, becoming creamy in old age. The stem is cylindrical, up to 30 mm wide, firm, full, white, becoming slightly brown in old age. The flesh is white, firm, juicy, with an intensive floury smell and cucumber taste. It grows abundantly from April to June in all woodlands mostly in grass on borders, next to paths, in gardens, parks, under deciduous trees and bushes. In certain places it is also found in grassy areas. It grows in lowland and foothill areas. It is one of the popular edible mushrooms, more so because of its early occurrence in the season. The young mushroom is often confused with the Blushing Inocybe, which is a bit smaller, and its gills redden when older or if injured. Remember: the St. George's Mushroom must always have whitish, very dense, conspicuously low gills and be sinuate and decurrent at the stem. It differs from the Blushing Inocybe in its intense, pleasant floury smell.

See also page 135 for more about the St. George's Mushroom.

The young fruit body of the St. George's Mushroom

☠ Godey's Inocybe

Cortinariaceae

Inocybe godeyi Gill.

The cap measures 20 to 50 mm in diameter, is bluntly bell-shaped at first, later flatly arched or completely flat with a blunt, rounded knob. The skin is silky and fibrous; when older or if pressed whitish and red spots appear. The cap margin is torn. The gills are thick, free, whitish at first, later olive-brown to rusty in colour with white edges, and if pressed red spots appear. The stem is cylindrical, only 10 mm wide and at the base it has a prominent, bulging bulb. It is silky fibrous, hoary white, later red flesh-coloured. The flesh is white, becoming reddish when injured and in old age, with a slightly fruity smell (sometimes even a light sperm-like smell) and of an indistinctive taste. It grows from June to September in deciduous and coniferous woodlands mostly in limy soils. It grows, but not in great abundance, mostly under oaks and hornbeams. It is a poisonous mushroom with a smaller content of muscarine than the Blushing Inocybe. In youth it is often confused with the Fairy-Ring Champignon and causes a slight muscarine type of poisoning if consumed.

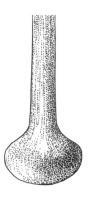

The cylindrical stem of Godey's Inocybe ends with a highly prominent bulging bulb.

Fairy-Ring Champignon

Marasmius oreades (Bolt. ex Fr.) Fr.

The cap is 15 to 35 mm wide, at first bluntly cylindrical or convex, later flat with a blunt knob in the middle, finely grooved from the translucent gills at the margin, otherwise smooth, tan or light flesh-coloured, darker when moist. The gills are very sparse, thick, high and sinuate at the stem and slightly lighter in colour than the cap. The stem is cylindrical, long, thin, full, hoary, light ochre, white and tomentose at the base, flexible, and very tough, even unbreakable. The flesh is whitish, very thin, with a pleasant taste and bitter almond-like smell. It grows from May to October in grassy places – on boundaries, meadows, in gardens and grassy woods – from lowland to mountainous regions. It is an excellent edible mushroom suitable for soups. Only the caps should be picked. When picking in the forest each fruit body should be properly examined. Do not forget that the Fairy-Ring Champignon has sparse gills, a flexible thin stem and a pleasant bitter almond-like smell which no inocybe mushroom has.

The Fairy-Ring Champignon has a cylindrical, long and thin stem.

Crown Fungus

Sarcosphaera crassa (Santi ex Steud.) Pouz.

The fruit body appears like a hollow ball at first and beneath the soil it grows to a diameter of 20 mm. When it comes out at the surface, it breaks up at the apex into four to eight irregular ends resembling a tulip. The inner, fertile part of the fruit body is light violet at first and then violet-brown in old age. The outer, sterile part of the fruit body is whitish at first, later ochre and finally violet-brown and tomentose. The stem does not usually develop. The flesh is fragile, gristly, white, up to 5 mm thick with an inconspicuous taste and slightly carbolic smell. It grows, but rarely, from May to June in coniferous and mixed woodlands, often on heavy clay soils from lowlands to foothills. This beautiful mushroom is moderately poisonous and should not be eaten.

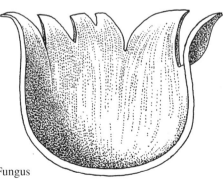

A cross-section of the Crown Fungus

Pig's Ears
Discina perlata (Fr.) Fr.

Veined Brown Cup Fungus
Disciotis venosa (Pers.) Boud.

Common Dung Cup
Peziza vesiculosa Bull. ex St. Am.

Pig's Ears

The fruit body grows up to 50 to 120 mm in size, is cup-shaped and flat in old age, lobed, with folds, whitish on the underside, and tobacco brown inside. It grows on a short stem to which it is attached by its divergent ridges. It normally grows from April to May in coniferous woodlands directly from rotting coniferous tree stumps. It is a good edible mushroom. It differs from the Crown Fungus in its smaller size and never has a violet hymenium.

Veined Brown Cup Fungus

The fruit body is 60 to 200 mm in size, ochre to yellow-brown, lobed and flat with folds, the underside reddish with radially and rootlike divergent ridges. The stem is very short and buried in the ground. The flesh is brittle, tough, waxy with an indistinctive taste and carbolic smell. It grows but rarely, from April to May on grassy warm sites, usually from the remains of the butterbur. It is a tasty edible mushroom and never has a violet hymenium.

Common Dung Cup

The fruit body is 30 to 100 mm in size. When young it looks like a hollow marble growing close to the ground, but gradually the opening on the apex expands until a thin-walled light ochre cup appears. In old age it turns into a wrinkled disc. It grows in summer from organic remains on manured soil. It is edible and differs from the Crown Fungus again by the fact that its hymenium is not violet.

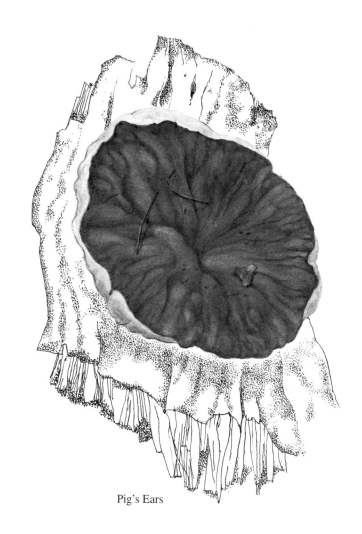

Pig's Ears

Veined Brown Cup Fungus

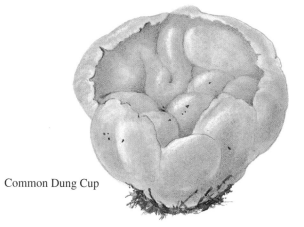

Common Dung Cup

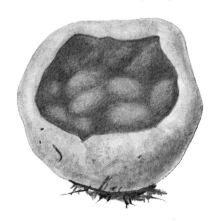

☠ Gemmed Amanita; Jonquil Amanita

Amanita gemmata (Fr.) Gill.

The cap measures 25 to 90 mm in diameter, is convex at first but soon becomes broadly arched to flat, is straw or light-ochre in colour, turning pale with age, and is grooved on the margin. It has viscid skin when moist, and shiny when dry, can be peeled, and is sparsely covered with irregular whitish scabs coming from the outer skin of the mushroom. The gills are dense, rounded, permanently pure white and free. The stem is erect, can be broken off, and has a cylindrical ending with thick bulb at the base that is covered with a low and thin volva. The upper third of the stem consists of a fine white membranous ring that falls off. The flesh is white, yellowish on the underside of the cap with an inconspicuous smell and a mild radish-like taste. It grows from June to October in deciduous and coniferous woodlands particularly in sandy pine woods and on the banks of ponds from lowland to foothill areas. It does not grow in great abundance and is not common to all regions. It may cause poisoning with mild symptoms.

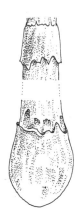

The Gemmed Amanita/Jonquil Amanita has a white membranous ring that falls off on the upper part of the stem; the bottom part of the stem ends in a thick bulb covered in a small volva.

Horse Mushroom

Agaricus arvensis Schaeff. ex Fr.

The cap is egg-shaped when young, pure white in colour, with a silky lustre, and dry on the surface. With age or after being touched it slowly turns yellow; it can grow to 50 to 140 mm wide. The gills stay pale for a long time, later becoming flesh-grey, chocolate and finally black-brown in colour; they are dense and free, at first covered with a membranous white veil changing with age into a protruding membranous, flaky white or yellowish ring at the bottom. The stem is quite long, can be broken off, is cylindrical, coming out into a broad bulbous base, is smooth, hollow and white with age. The flesh is white with a pleasant aniseed-like smell. It has a better taste than cultivated champignons. It grows from May till autumn in deciduous, mixed and coniferous woodlands with adequate humus. It is rarely found in meadows and orchards. It is an excellent edible mushroom and is sold in markets. It is a versatile mushroom for cooking. The Horse Mushroom can easily be distinguished from the Gemmed Amanita/Jonquil Amanita because its gills go dark in old age, it has an aniseed smell, there is no volva at the bottom of the stem and the cap yellows once it has been touched.

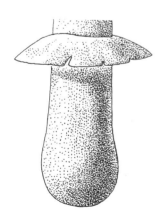

The Horse Mushroom also has a white membranous ring at the top of the stem; the bottom of the stem turns into a broad bulb but it never has a volva.

☠ Fool's Mushroom; White Death Cap

Amanita verna (Bull.) Pers.

The cap measures 60 to 120 mm in diameter; it is convex at first, later becoming bell-shaped, arched or gently arched, pure white in colour, with a silky lustre, viscid when moist and smooth. The gills are dense, white and adnexed. The stem is cylindrical, slightly broader at the base growing from a white free volva, smooth, naked with a pendent ring on its upper third part. The flesh is white, with a pleasant smell at first and later becoming unpleasant, but of an excellent taste. The Fool's Mushroom/White Death Cap therefore entices the picker by its appearance, taste and smell. It grows (but is rare), from June to October, usually in deciduous woods on lower sites. Some experts consider it to be the white variety of the green Death Cap. It can easily be mistaken for certain species of champignons or parasol mushrooms and the poison of the Fool's Mushroom/White Death Cap is as dangerous as that of the green Death Cap.

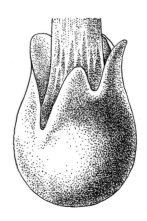

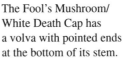
The Fool's Mushroom/
White Death Cap has
a volva with pointed ends
at the bottom of its stem.

Smooth Parasol

Leucoagaricus leucothites (Vitt.) P.D. Orton

Horse Mushroom

Agaricus arvensis Schaeff. ex Fr.

Smooth Parasol

The cap is 50 to 100 mm wide, white, pinkish when young, later becoming smooth. The gills are white when young and later turn pink. The stem can be broken off, and is white, smooth, hollow and cylindrical. The ring is weak, small and cannot be moved. The flesh is always pure white, with a strong fruity smell and a pleasant taste. It is scattered in growth from August to October on grassy sites, in fields and woodland borders. It is one of the popular edible mushrooms. It can best be distinguished from the Fool's Mushroom/White Death Cap by its pinkish gills and because it has no volva on the bottom part of its stem.

Horse Mushroom

The cap is 50 to 140 mm wide; oval at first, then arched or gently arched with age, whitish or creamy, and yellowish in places where it has been pressed. The gills are dense, free, light for a long time then becoming fleshy grey and eventually black-brown with age. The stem is cylindrical and white with a membranous ring on its upper third part. The flesh is soft, white, with a pleasant mushroom taste and distinctive aniseed smell. It grows in abundance from May to October in coniferous and mixed woodlands rich in humus, from lowlands to higher areas. It is one of the popular edible mushrooms which can be cooked in various ways. It can be distinguished from the Fool's Mushroom/ White Death Cap above all by the fact that it has no volva and no constant white gills.

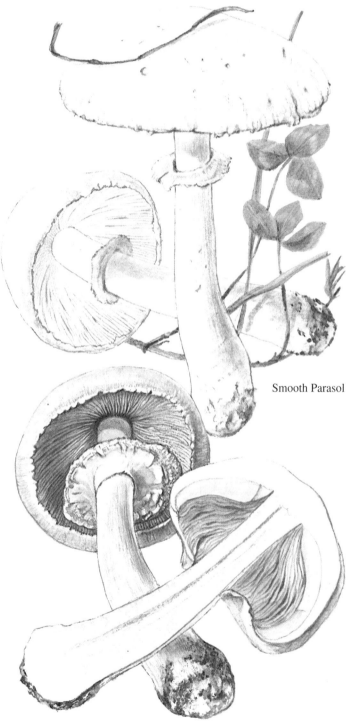

Smooth Parasol

Horse Mushroom

Neither the Smooth Parasol (left) nor the Horse Mushroom (right) has a volva.

☠ Pointed Inocybe

Inocybe fastigiata (Schaeff. ex Fr.) Quél.

The cap is 30 to 60 mm wide, narrowly conical when young and broadly arched with age, with a sharp prominent knob, ochre to brown in colour with distinctive radial fibres, and grooves soon with radial cracks appearing, and thin flesh. The gills are free, moderately dense, paunchy, whitish when young, later becoming olive-yellow to brownish and whitish on the edges. The stem is cylindrical, sometimes slightly thicker at the base, full, fibrous, whitish with white flakes at the top. The flesh is quite meaty, whitish, with an indistinctive taste and sperm-like smell. It grows quite abundantly from June to October in coniferous and deciduous woodlands, on woodland paths and in ditches from lowlands to foothills. It is one of the mushrooms containing a great amount of muscarine so it can cause serious poisoning. It is very changeable and, therefore, a dangerous species. Beware of mistaking it for the Fairy-Ring Champignon, the Wood Agaric/Common Collybia/Oak-Loving Collybia, laccarias and other smaller mushrooms. Look out for certain important characteristics such as the sperm-like smell, the certain type of gills and the shape of the cap which is typical of the inocybe mushrooms.

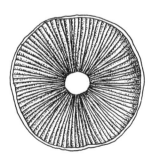

The underside of the cap of the Pointed Inocybe

Fairy-Ring Champignon
Marasmius oreades (Bolt. ex Fr.) Fr.

¶¶

Wood Agaric; Common Collybia; Oak-Loving Collybia
Collybia dryophila (Bull. ex Fr.) Kumm.

¶¶

Fairy-Ring Champignon
There is a detailed description of the Fairy-Ring Champignon on pages 33 and 73. It can be distinguished from the Pointed Inocybe by its almond-like smell and flexible stem.

Wood Agaric; Common Collybia; Oak-Loving Collybia
The cap measures 20 to 40 mm in diameter, it is convex with an inrolled margin when young but soon becomes broadly arched and even depressed. There are folds on the margins, it is light-ochre or yellow-brown, and smooth with thin flesh. The gills are very dense, thin, sinuately attached to the stem, white and later becoming light-cream. The stem is erect, thin, tubular, smooth, bald, ochre or red-brown in colour. The flesh is very thin, whitish, with pleasant slight mushroom taste and smell. It grows from May to October in various plant communities from lowland to mountainous areas. Under favourable weather conditions it can grow in great abundance. It is a really useful mushroom for cooking purposes but only the caps of young fruit bodies are picked. The Wood Agaric/Common Collybia/Oak-Loving Collybia can be distinguished from the Inocybe by its pleasant mushroom smell and very dense gills.

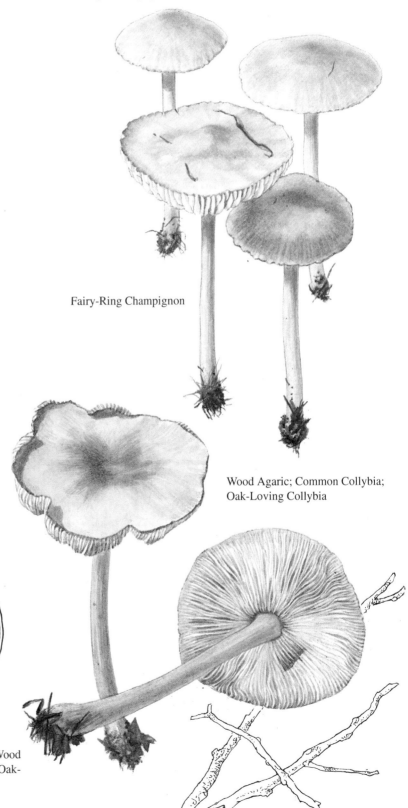

Fairy-Ring Champignon

Wood Agaric; Common Collybia; Oak-Loving Collybia

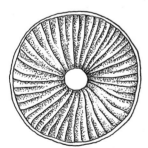

The sparse gills of the Fairy-Ring Champignon

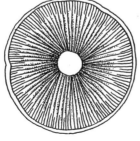

The very dense gills of the Wood Agaric/Common Collybia/Oak-Loving Collybia

☠ Rose Grey Entoloma

Entoloma rhodopolium (Fr.) Kumm.

The cap is 40 to 100 mm wide, bell-shaped when young with a thickly inrolled margin, later arched to flat with a blunt knob and depressed in the middle, a dirty-ochre, grey-brown colour, with ingrown fibres, shiny when dry and viscid when moist, bald and darkening. The gills are sparse, quite high, sinuately attached to the stem, whitish when young but soon becoming pinkish and fleshy pink with age. The stem is cylindrical, tough, full and silky white. The flesh is whitish, with a cucumber taste and smell. It grows from July to October, scattered in deciduous woodlands, groves and orchards, most often under beeches and hornbeams. It is less poisonous than the Leaden Entoloma (see page 108), but does cause poisoning which leads to vomiting and diarrhoea. It looks a lot like the edible Buckler Agaric but grows somewhat later. In view of the fact that there is danger of confusing the two species, never pick the Buckler Agaric in parks and woodlands. It is recommended picking the Buckler Agaric only in orchards under trees of the Rosea genus of plants.

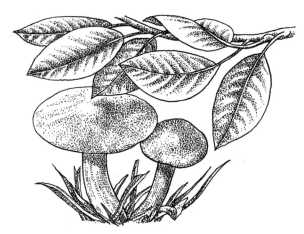

The Rose Grey Entoloma grows in deciduous woodlands often under beeches and hornbeams.

Buckler Agaric

Entoloma clypeatum (L. ex Hook.) Kumm.

The cap measures 30 to 120 mm in diameter; when young it is bell-shaped with an inrolled margin, soon becoming broadly arched with a rounded knob; the skin is darker and viscid when moist, and lighter, shiny, whitish to grey-brown when dry. The gills are sparse, whitish when young, then turning pink. The stem is cylindrical often with folds, firm, fibrous, whitish and shiny. The flesh is whitish to greyish, with a cucumber taste and smell. It grows from April to June in orchards, parks and gardens under trees of the Rosea genus (cherry, blackthorn, plum, pear, apple, hawthorn) usually in big clumps. Experts divide it into several new species particularly according to the types of trees under which it grows. This division is not important when using the mushroom for cooking purposes as all the species are edible. Be careful not to pick the Buckler Agaric under a beech or hornbeam growing in woodlands or parks because the poisonous Rose Grey Entoloma, which is very similar to the Buckler Agaric, also grows there.

Pick the Buckler Agaric only under trees or bushes of the Rosea genus.

☠ Flat-Top Agaricus

Agaricus meleagris J. Schaeff.

The cap measures 50 to 110 mm in diameter, is almost bell-shaped at first, later becoming arched, is flat at the apex. It is ochre grey-brown to smoky black, sometimes clay brown in colour, soon cracking into flattened scales which are arranged into a regular rooflike shape and dark brown, grey-brown to smoky-black in colour. The translucent flesh between the scales is whitish. The gills are almost white when young, later pink with ripening spores turning red-chocolate to black in colour; they are quite dense and free. The stem is cylindrical, thicker at the base and sometimes with a bulging bulb, often curved at the bottom while the upper third has a large thinly membranous ring becoming pendent with age. The flesh is white and quite dense within the cap. When cut at the base it is conspicuously orange-yellow in colour with a sourish, though not unpleasant, taste. The carbolic smell becomes apparent mainly when cooked. It grows from July to September in mixed woodlands but is rare. It is not suitable for cooking purposes as it is mildly poisonous, causing digestive problems.

The Flat-Top Agaricus has a thin, membranous ring which is double at first.

Large Grey Agaric; Shaggy Parasol

Macrolepiota rhacodes (Vitt.) Sing.

Prince

Agaricus augustus Fr.

Large Grey Agaric; Shaggy Parasol

The cap is 90 to 140 mm wide, convex, later becoming arched to flat, densely covered in large protruding brownish scales. The gills are dense, high, white and redden when injured. The stem is cylindrical and widens at the base into a bulb, easily breakable, white when young and turning brownish with age, with a membranous ring. The flesh is white, reddens when injured and has a pleasant taste and mushroom smell. It grows quite abundantly from June to October in mixed woodlands. It is an excellent edible mushroom. It can be safely distinguished from the Flat-Top Agaricus by its white gills and pleasant-smelling flesh.

Prince

The cap is 100 to 250 mm wide; convex when young and becoming flat later, straw-coloured and covered in rusty-brown flattened scales. The gills are dense, free, grey-white, becoming chocolate-coloured with age. The stem is cylindrical and robust, white then later straw-coloured, can be broken off and has a big ring. The flesh is white, of a delicious taste and pleasant aniseed smell. It grows rarely from July to October in warmed deciduous and coniferous woodlands. It is one of the excellent edible mushrooms with an intensive mushroom aniseed smell which is the main characteristic that distinguishes it from the Flat-Top Agaricus.

Large Grey Agaric; Shaggy Parasol

Prince

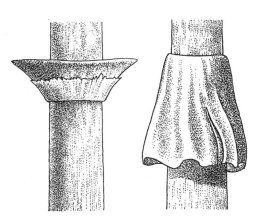

The Large Grey Agaric/Shaggy Parasol (left) has a white, cotton wool-like ring that is free and can be moved along the stem. The Prince (right) has a big, softly membranous ring that is smooth on the surface and flaky on the underside and hangs down like a skirt.

45

☠ Yellow-Staining Agaricus

Agaricus xanthoderma Gen.

The cap measures 50 to 150 mm in diameter, is convex to acorn-shaped when young, becoming flat with age, fibrillose to tomentose, sometimes with shelf-like cracks, white and turning lemon-yellow when pressed. The gills are dense, free, pale-coloured when young, becoming pink-violet, amber-brown with age. The gills are at first concealed by a veil which later turns into a whitish membranous ring. The stem can be broken off, is cylindrical and broadens into a spherical bulb at the base, and is white, turning a rich lemon yellow colour when pressed. The flesh is white, but turns yellow immediately (mainly at the base) when cut. It has an unpleasant carbolic smell which increases when cooked, and a sweet tannic taste. It grows from June to October, scattered in deciduous woodlands, groves and parks. It grows abundantly on limestone ground in spruce woods. It is poisonous and causes stomach problems, vomiting and discomfort.

The bottom part of the stem of the Yellow-Staining Agaricus broadens out into a spherical bulb. When injured it turns a rich lemon-yellow colour while giving off a carbolic smell.

Field Mushroom

Agaricus campestris L. ex Fr.

Horse Mushroom

Agaricus arvensis Schaeff. ex Fr.

Field Mushroom

The cap measures 40 to 120 mm in diameter, at first spherical and inrolled at the margin, later becoming arched to flat, white, silken fibrous, naked, rarely also with brownish scales at the apex. The gills are dense, sinuate and paunchy at the stem, pink when young and later turning black-brown. The stem is cylindrical, full, smooth, whitish, and has a membranous ring in the upper third. The flesh is white and turns a pale pink when cut, has a delicious smell and taste. It grows from May to November on well-manured meadows, on pastures, fields and grassy paths. It is one of the excellent edible mushrooms. It can easily be distinguished from the Yellow-Staining Agaricus because it does not have a carbolic smell.

Horse Mushroom

The cap is 50 to 140 mm wide; oval when young and later arched to flat, and whitish or cream, and yellowish when pressed. The gills are dense, free, remain light for a long time and turn black-brown when old; they are never pink. The stem is cylindrical, and white with a membranous ring on the upper third. The flesh is soft, white, with a pleasant mushroom taste and a distinctive aniseed smell. It grows abundantly from June to October in coniferous and mixed woodlands rich in humus, from lowlands to higher areas. It is one of the more popular edible mushrooms. It can be distinguished from the Yellow-Staining Agaricus by its aniseed smell.

Field Mushroom

The bottom part of the stem of the Field Mushroom or the Horse Mushroom

Horse Mushroom

☠ **Grey Mottle-Gill**

Panaeolus sphinctrinus (Fr.) Quél.

The cap is 15 to 30 mm wide, parabolic, permanently bell-shaped, shiny with white appendices (remains of the veil) on the margin, with a grey or grey-brown surface. The gills are high and grey at first, protruding, when older with black specks from the unequally ripening spores. The spores form circular zones and look like speckled stains. This is how the species got its name. This characteristic can be used to distinguish it from other mushroom species. The edges of the gills are whitish in old age. The stem is very long, grooved on top, slender, erect, tough, fragile, hollow, dusty and hoary and reddish brown. The flesh is very thin, fragile, brownish, with no distinctive taste and smell.

A cross-section of the fruit body of the Grey Mottle-Gill

Fairy-Ring Champignon

Marasmius oreades (Bolt. ex Fr.) Fr.

A detailed description of the Fairy-Ring Champignon is given on pages 33 and 73. Although the Fairy-Ring Champignon grows on similar grassy sites to the Grey Mottle-Gill, it can be easily distinguished by its cap, gills and stem. Particularly distinctive is the difference in the gills which are tan (never speckled) on a Fairy-Ring Champignon, whereas the gills on the Grey Mottle-Gill grow dark and speckled in old age. The stem of the Fairy-Ring Champignon is firm, tough and unbreakable, whereas that of the Grey Mottle-Gill is very long, thin and fragile. When shaking, the fruit body of the Fairy-Ring Champignon moves like rubber. The fruit body of the Grey Mottle-Gill breaks immediately when shaken.

A cross-section of the Fairy-Ring Champignon – the gills are sparse and light (never speckled).

☠ False Death Cap

Amanita citrina (Schaeff.) ex Roques

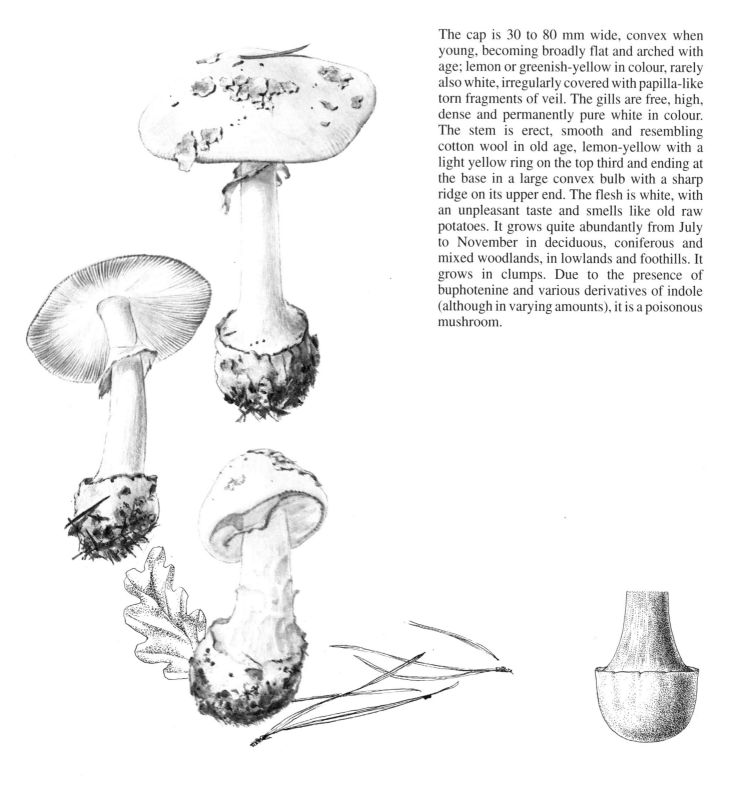

The cap is 30 to 80 mm wide, convex when young, becoming broadly flat and arched with age; lemon or greenish-yellow in colour, rarely also white, irregularly covered with papilla-like torn fragments of veil. The gills are free, high, dense and permanently pure white in colour. The stem is erect, smooth and resembling cotton wool in old age, lemon-yellow with a light yellow ring on the top third and ending at the base in a large convex bulb with a sharp ridge on its upper end. The flesh is white, with an unpleasant taste and smells like old raw potatoes. It grows quite abundantly from July to November in deciduous, coniferous and mixed woodlands, in lowlands and foothills. It grows in clumps. Due to the presence of buphotenine and various derivatives of indole (although in varying amounts), it is a poisonous mushroom.

The base of the stem of the False Death Cap ends in a bulb. The cotton wool-like bulb is sharply cut off at the top.

Common Volvariella

Volvariella speciosa (Fr.) Sing.

The cap is 60 to 120 mm in diameter, conically bell-shaped when young, becoming flat with age, with a blunt knob in the middle, smooth, viscid, shiny when dry, dirty-white, greyish to brownish. The gills are dense, wide, free at the stem, white when young, becoming fleshy pink with age. The stem is cylindrical, full, white, covered with a free whitish volva, and broadens out at the base into a bulb. The flesh is meaty, white, with an indistinctive taste and honey potato-like smell. It is scattered in growth and grows from May to September on heavily manured soil outside woods, in gardens, fields, near compost and in parks, on lowlands and foothills. It is one of the edible mushrooms. It is more popular in eastern cuisines where one of the species of *Volvariella* is even artifically cultivated. It can easily be distinguished from the False Death Cap by the fleshy pink colour of its gills in old age, well developed volva and absence of a ring on its stem.

The base of the stem of the Common Volvariella broadens out into a bulb and is covered with a white volva which disappears in old age. When the mushroom is pulled up from the substrate, the volva often remains in the ground.

☠ Fly Agaric

Amanita muscaria (L. ex Fr.) Hook.

The cap is 50 to 200 mm wide, almost spherical when young but soon becoming flat with a grooved margin, of a bright-scarlet or orange-red colour and covered in whitish or yellowish remains of the veil which disappears after long rains, leaving the surface smooth, viscid and shiny when dry. The gills are white, free and quite dense. The stem is erect, cylindrical, up to 250 mm long with a smooth ring at the top, white flaky, with a spherical bulb at the base covered with several rings of whitish papillae. The flesh is white, orange under the skin, with a sweetish nutty taste and an indistinctive smell. It grows from the end of June to October in mixed woodlands. Due to the presence of muscarine it is one of the poisonous mushrooms and its mycoatropine content can also cause mental disorders. It can be confused with Caesar's Amanita and the Blusher Amanita. When very young its fruit bodies are still spherical and covered with a whitish veil so it can be easily mistaken for certain species of puffball mushrooms. It is very easy to distinguish from the puffball by cutting up a fruit body. When the fruit body is like cottage cheese and pure white inside, without any signs of a stem, and has gills and an orange skin at the apex, then it is one of the puffball mushrooms.

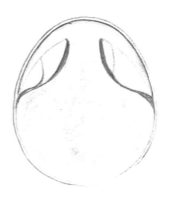

The formation of the stem with the gills can be seen clearly on the cross-section of the young fruit bodies of the Fly Agaric; the Fly Agaric always has orange flesh at the apex under the surface of the outer skin.

Caesar's Amanita

Amanita caesarea (Scop. ex Fr.) Grev.

Blusher

Amanita rubescens (Pers. ex Fr.) S.F. Gray

Caesar's Amanita

This is a rare mushroom found during the summer in deciduous woodlands on warmer sites. The cap has red, naked gills and the stem is a beautiful golden yellow colour. The flesh is yellowish with a pleasant taste and distinctive smell. The stem is always covered at the base with a large white membranous volva. In ancient Rome, this mushroom was an essential ingredient in feasts. These days it is scarce and deserves protection. It can easily be distinguished from the Fly Agaric by its golden-yellow gills and stem.

Blusher

A detailed description is given on page 55. In the last few decades the tasty Blusher has become a very popular mushroom, particularly in towns and cities. It can only be confused with the lighter-coloured fruit bodies of the poisonous Fly Agaric. Otherwise the skin of the cap of the Blusher is never a distinctive red, only pink or slightly fleshy-red. The Blusher can also be safely recognised by its flesh turning pink at the base of the stem, particularly distinctive on a mushroom infested with insects.

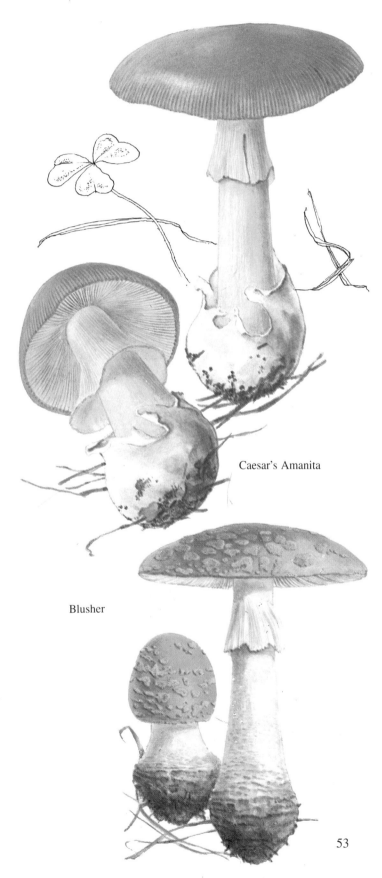

Caesar's Amanita

Blusher

A cross-section of puffball mushrooms shows that they are like cottage cheese and white inside.

Common Puffball; Warted Puffball; Gemmed Puffball

53

☠ False Blusher; Panther Amanita

Amanita pantherina (D.C. ex Fr.) Krombh.

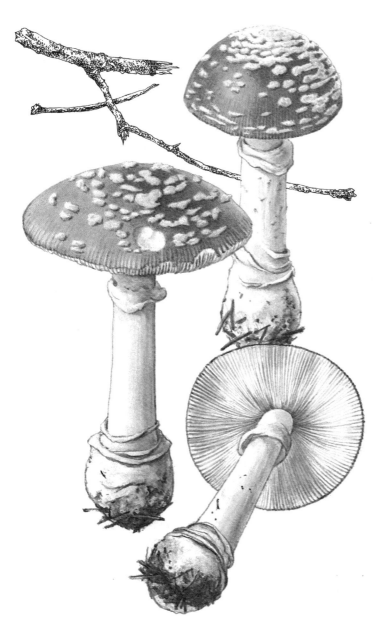

The cap is 40 to 100 mm wide, spherical when young, becoming rounded and broadly arched to flat with age, greyish, grey-brown, yellow-brown to olive-brown, with distinctive grooves on the margin covered with tiny whitish scabs concentrated into rings. After long rains the surface becomes naked. The gills are dense, white, rounded and free at the stem. The stem is breakable, cylindrical, erect, and white with a smooth white ring at the top that is limp and disappears in old age. The base of the stem broadens out into a bulb which is lined with a white border. White rings are sometimes found lying obliquely above the bulb. The flesh is white, with a slight potato or indistinctive taste and smell. The smell becomes unpleasant and sweetish when the mushroom wilts. It grows from July to October in deciduous and coniferous woodlands, on forest borders and under individual trees. In places it grows in abundance, particularly in warmer regions. It only takes a small amount to cause mycoatropine poisoning, with serious effects.

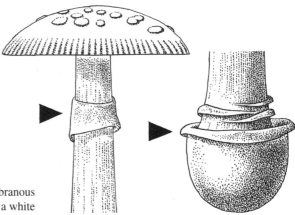

The False Blusher/Panther Amanita has a membranous ungrooved ring and a stem ending in a bulb with a white border.

Blusher

Amanita rubescens (Pers. ex Fr.) S. F. Gray

The cap measures 40 to 180 mm in diameter, is convex when young, later becoming arched to flat, with easy-to-peel skin, pink, meaty red with numerous whitish torn fragments of a veil which covers the young fruit body. In rain the surface of the cap of the fruit body is bald and slightly viscid. The gills are free and fragile; red specks appear with age and when injured they turn pink. The stem is cylindrical, breakable, whitish on top, reddish on the bottom, smooth or flaky, full, tubular and hollow with age, broadening out at the base into a bulb covered with several rings of small papillae. On young mushrooms the gills are covered with an adnate whitish veil. When the cap opens out, the veil is torn away thus forming the clear grooves on the ring. The ring remains on the stem until the fruit body gets very old. The flesh is white, red when injured. Those places disturbed by insect larvae become pink. The flesh has a pleasant mushroom taste that is slightly sweet and the smell is indistinctive. It grows a lot from June to November in all woodlands in lowlands and foothills. This is one of the excellent edible mushrooms which can be used for cooking in many ways. It can be easily distinguished from the False Blusher/Panther Amanita mainly by its clearly grooved ring.

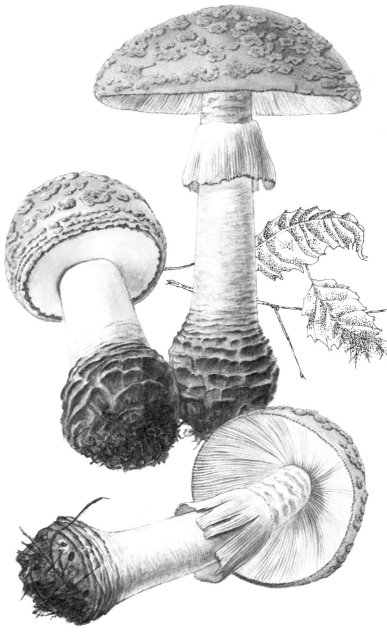

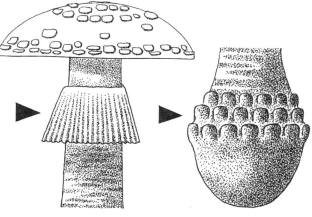

The Blusher has a clearly grooved ring and a broad bulbous stem covered with several rings of small papillae.

☠ **Death Cap**

Amanita phalloides (Fr.) Link

This is one of the most poisonous mushrooms. It usually grows from July to October in deciduous and mixed woodlands. In warmer summers, it appears in May and grows till November. It can even be found in cultivated spruce woods planted after the felling of deciduous trees. It also grows outside woodlands, for example in the middle of a park where there is one oak tree. An important characteristic for recognising the Death Cap is the broad base of the stem and the membranous, somewhat free, volva which encompasses the base like a stocking. The white volva with pointed ends at the top is the remainder of the cover which conceals the entire young fruit body. When the mushroom starts to grow, the cover is torn and the cap – free of the scabs – slips out. To identify the Death Cap or a similar species, always carefully remove the entire mushroom from the soil otherwise the stem gets torn and the bulbous base with the volva remains in the ground. A detailed description and further illustration of the Death Cap are also found on pages 58 and 60.

The base of the stem of the Death Cap grows from a big membranous volva which is popularly called the Cup of Death.

Greenish Russula; Quilted-Green Russula

Russula virescens (Schaeff. ex Zanted.) Fr.

Grass-Green Russula; Green Russula

Russula aeruginea Lindbl. in Fr.

Greenish Russula; Quilted-Green Russula

Greenish Russula; Quilted-Green Russula

The cap is 60 to 140 mm wide, and convex at first, becoming long arched, flat and depressed with age. The skin is dry and cannot be peeled off, is velvet with grained grooves on the margin with shelf-like cracks appearing with age. It its white when young, later acquiring a coppery-green colour that goes pale with age with rusty speckles. The gills are rounded, white, dense, becoming creamy-coloured with age. The stem is robust, erect, firm, white and turns rusty in old age. The flesh is white, has a delicious nutty taste and a pleasant fruity smell. It grows from June to October in all woodlands, mainly under deciduous trees. It is one of the tastiest edible mushrooms.

Grass-Green Russula; Green Russula

The cap is 30 to 100 mm in diameter, convex when young, later becoming flat and depressed; green or olive-green, brownish in the middle, with thin meat, naked, viscid when moist with a skin that peels off well. The gills are dense, rounded, fragile, and white becoming straw-coloured to rusty with age. The stem is cylindrical, fragile, white, rusty-coloured at the base and resembling cotton wool in old age. The flesh is white, rusty in old age with an indistinctive smell and a stinging to burning taste; once cooked however, the sting disappears. It grows abundantly in summer and autumn under birches and spruces in acid soils, on woodland paths and under individual trees. Both Russulas – the Greenish/Quilted-Green and the Grass-Green/Green – can easily be distinguished from the Death Cap by the fact that they have no volva or ring.

Neither the Greenish/Quilted-Green Russula nor the Grass-Green/Green Russula has a volva at the base of its stems.

Grass-Green Russula; Green Russula

☠ **Death Cap**

Amanita phalloides (Fr.) Link

The cap is brownish to yellow-green, green or pale to whitish yellow, normally smooth. The colouring is not always the same. Some fruit bodies are olive-green, others greyish-green, sometimes even lemon-coloured. The cap is egg-shaped in youth, later becoming bell-shaped and finally flat. The cap measures 70 to 150 mm in diameter and there are always white, dense and rather wide, paunchy gills on the underside that are rounded at the stem. They never go dark. In youth the gills are covered with a thin membrane which joins together the margin of the cap with the top part of the stem. Once the cap grows and expands, it tears the membrane and its remains form a limp white ring. The stem is slender, white, yellow-green or greyish, cracked on the surface into scales forming stripes and ending in a large spherical bulb which is always enveloped in a white semi-free, quite high volva with pointed ends. The flesh is permanently pure white, slightly ochre on the underside of the cap, with a delicious taste and a sweetish, fine potato-like smell; when the mushroom begins drying up it has a potent sweetish smell of rotting flowers or maturing cheese. Death Cap is deadly poisonous so beware of confusing it with the Firwood Agaric/Man On Horseback or a champignon.

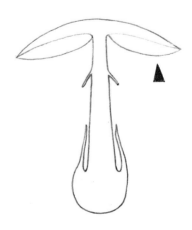

White gills, a volva and ring can be seen on a cross-section of the fruit body of a Death Cap.

Firwood Agaric; Man On Horseback

Tricholoma flavovirens (Pers. ex Fr.) Lund.

Horse Mushroom

Agaricus arvensis Schaeff. ex Fr.

Firwood Agaric; Man On Horseback

The cap is 30 to 90 mm wide; arched with an inrolled margin when young, becoming flatly arched and with quite a lot of folds with age; yellow-brown and viscid when moist. The gills are sinuate and decurrent at the stem and sulphur yellow in colour. The stem is cylindrical, with fine fibres and sulphur yellow in colour. The flesh is whitish with a floury smell and a pleasant taste of sweet nuts. It grows in the autumn, mostly in sandy pine woods, often in large clumps. It differs from the Death Cap in its yellow gills.

Horse Mushroom

The cap measures 50 to 140 mm in diameter, is club-shaped when young but soon becoming broadly arched and finally completely flat, with a smooth, bald skin that has a silky lustre and is white, but goes yellow when pressed and with age, eventually becoming coloured like the lighter fruit bodies of the Death Cap. The gills are pale when young, later becoming fleshy-grey, chocolate and finally brown-black. The stem is cylindrical, broadening out into a small bulb at the base, and is hollow and white; there is a ring under the gills. The flesh is juicy, white, with a pleasant aniseed smell and a sweetish mushroom taste. When picking, take care to examine the colouring of the gills (the gills of the Death Cap remain white even in old age).

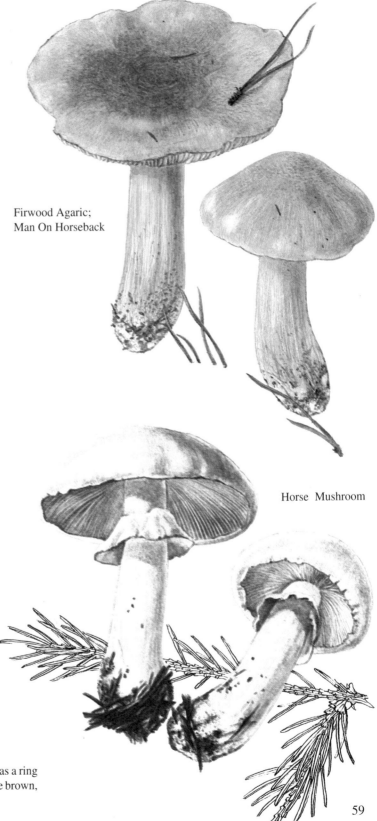

Firwood Agaric;
Man On Horseback

Horse Mushroom

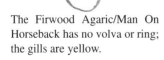

The Firwood Agaric/Man On Horseback has no volva or ring; the gills are yellow.

The Horse Mushroom has a ring but no volva; the gills are brown, pink in youth.

☠ **Death Cap**

Amanita phalloides (Fr.) Link

The botanical characteristics of the Death Cap and the main rules when identifying them have already been stated on previous pages (see also the illustrations). In view of the fact that the Death Cap is a very dangerous poisonous mushroom here are the main characteristics again. The colouring of the skin of the cap is very changeable – from green-yellow, olive-green, green-brown and even white in the white form of the Death Cap. The gills are permanently pure white. The stem ends in a large spherical soft bulb buried inside a free, high volva with conspicuously pointed ends. In the very early stage of growth the entire fruit body is encased in a white veil and looks like an egg. It is at this time that the Death Cap can easily be confused with one of the puffballs or the young Sheathed Agaric/Grisette. The older, lighter-coloured fruit bodies of the Death Cap can also often be mistaken for parasol mushrooms, so always look for the basic characteristics of the Parasol Mushroom (on the next page).

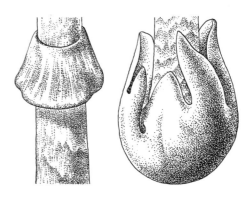

The stem of the Death Cap has a ring and a conspicuous membranous volva with pointed ends at the base.

Parasol Mushroom

Macrolepiota procera (Scop. ex Fr.) Sing.

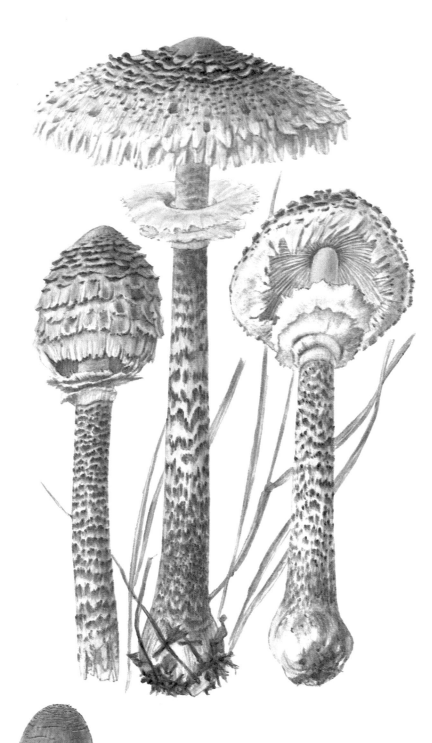

The cap is 100 to 300 mm wide, club-shaped and brownish when young, later becoming flat with a knob in the middle, covered in a tiled structure with large tomentose protruding, and brownish scales. The gills are white, dense, free, paunchy, quite high, protruding from the stem. The stem is breakable, up to 400 mm high, very narrow at the top, the base ending in a flat bulb, hollow, completely light brown when young, later becoming covered with diagonally striped scales, and conspicuously woody. On the upper third there is a large white leathery ring with a double edge which can be moved along the stem. The flesh is juicy when young but soon becomes cotton wool-like inside the cap; in the stem it is tough and fibrous, permanently white with a delicious mushroom taste and a pleasant sweetish smell. It grows from July to October in warm borders of all woodlands, clearings, alongside woodland paths and in grass in glades where it grows to a considerable size. Mushroom pickers surprisingly often mistake this big mushroom for the deadly poisonous Death Cap, so take note: the Parasol Mushroom has scales on the surface of its cap and has no volva around the bulb at the base of its stem.

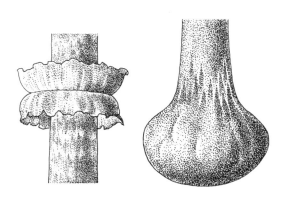

The Parasol Mushroom has a movable ring on its stem but never grows from a volva.

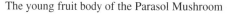

The young fruit body of the Parasol Mushroom

☠ # Royal Amanita

Amanita regalis (Fr.) Michael

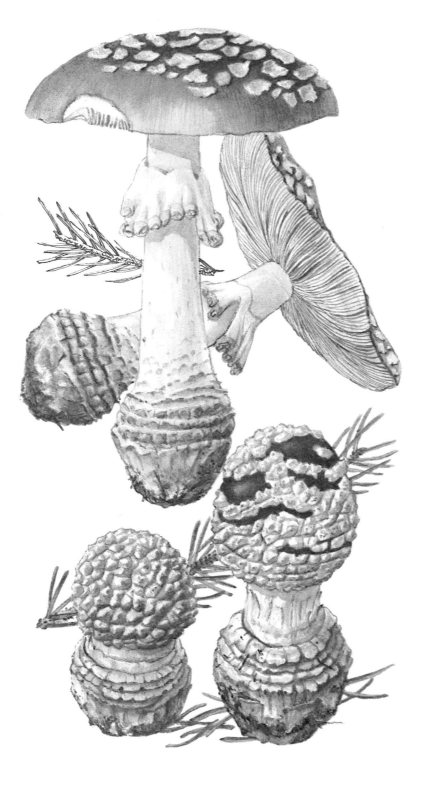

The cap is 70 to 200 mm wide, spherical when young, later becoming arched, then broadly flat, a bright liver yellow-brown colour, densely covered with yellowish to light ochre papillae arranged into concentrated rings, viscid when moist, shiny when dry; thin-fleshed with grooves on the margin when older. The gills are dense, free, white and lined with a creamy to yellowish shade at the edges. The stem is full, large, brittle, broadening at the base into a spherical bulb covered with several rings of small yellowish papillae. The surface of the stem is not white but a pale yellowish colour. The veil covering the gills in youth is membranous and yellow-ochre; in old age it changes into a large ochre-coloured ring often carrying several large papillae on its margin. The flesh is whitish, slightly yellowish inside the stem and golden-yellow on the underside of the cap, with a pleasant, nutty sweetish taste and indistinctive smell. It grows quite sparcely from July to October in foothill and mountain spruce woods. It contains similar poison to that of the Fly Agaric and should not be eaten.

Royal Amanita has a large ochre ring with several papillae on the margin.

Blusher
Amanita rubescens (Pers. ex Fr.) S.F. Gray

Stout Agaric
Amanita spissa (Fr.) Opiz

Blusher

The Blusher has been described in detail on page 55. Its typical characteristics are: the cap is 40 to 180 mm wide; the pink, fleshy-red skin can be easily peeled off and it has whitish torn fragments, the remains of the veil. The gills are white with black specks appearing in old age, and when injured they turn pink. The stem is whitish on top and reddish at the base broadening out into a bulb that is covered with several rings of small papillae. On the upper part of the stem there is a large whitish ring which is clearly grooved. The Blusher Amanita differs from the Royal Amanita above all in the fleshy pink to light red-brown surface of the cap and the pinkish flesh at the base of the stem.

Stout Agaric

The cap is 50 to 120 mm wide, spherical when young, later arched and then flat, grey or grey-brown, densely covered with whitish scabs. The gills are dense, white and free. The stem is cylindrical, ending in a conical bulb at the base; the upper part of the stem is whitish with a densely grooved ring. The flesh is white, tasting and smelling of old raw potatoes. It grows abundantly in the summer and autumn in all woodlands even in dry weather. It is an edible mushroom but is not picked very often because of its taste. It is easy to distinguish from the Royal Amanita by its grooved ring and the potato-smelling flesh.

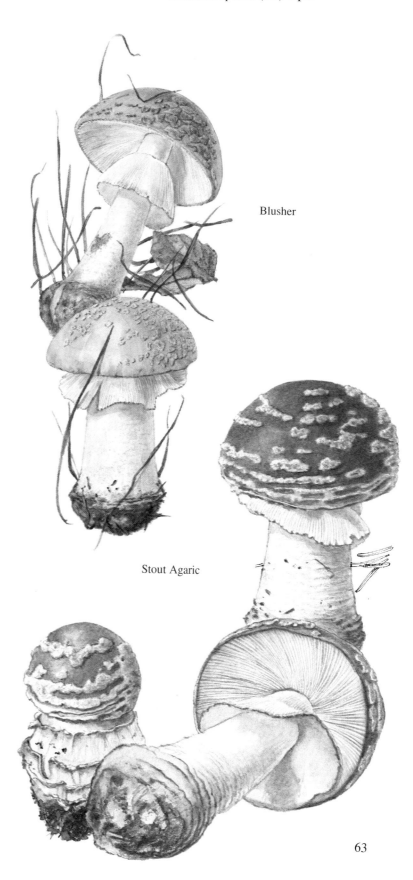

Blusher

Stout Agaric

The Blusher (left) and the Stout Agaric (right) have a clearly grooved ring.

☠ **Bitter Bolete**

Boletus calopus Fr.

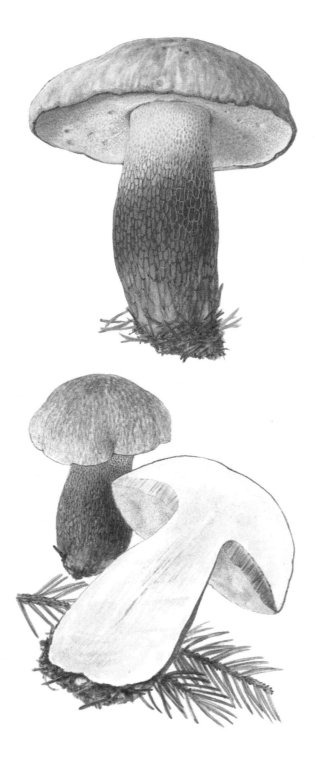

The cap is 40 to 150 mm wide, convex at first, later arched even cushion-like, subtomentose when young, later naked, pale-brown, olive-grey or ochre-brown in colour with the margin being inrolled for a long time and with irregular folds. The tubes are yellow and turn blue when touched, and sinuate at the stem. The mouth of the tubes is small, in a bright lemon-yellow colour. The stem is paunchy at first, later club-shaped, yellow with a fine white network on top, and elsewhere crimson-red in colour with a clear fleshy-red network, the loops of which get larger towards the brownish base. The flesh is hard, whitish and turns blue to a dirty-yellow colour when cut; it has an unpleasant sour smell and a very bitter, disgusting taste. It grows in summer and autumn mostly in foothill coniferous woodlands; on hilly land it can be found under beeches but can also grow high up in mountainous regions. It is a beautiful bolete in appearance but cannot be used of its taste. It is slightly poisonous, causing digestive problems and vomiting. It is mistaken for Devil's Boletus, Red-Stemmed Bolete and Pale Bolete.

The Bitter Bolete has a fine network on a yellow background on the upper part of its stem, but a fleshy red network on a crimson-red background on the bottom part.

Pale Bolete

Boletus luridus Schaeff. ex Fr.

Red-Stemmed Bolete

Boletus erythropus (Fr. ex Fr.) Pers.

Pale Bolete

The cap is 50 to 160 mm wide, convex when young, later arched or cushion-like and flat, olive-ochre, yellow-orange, with a velvet texture, dry. In places where it is pressed it goes dark or an intense blue colour. The tubes are yellow, red at the mouth and turn blue if touched. The stem is cylindrical, thickening out at the base into a club, red on the bottom half, yellow at the top, decorated with a conspicuous network with red loops. The flesh is yellow and goes clearly blue when injured, has a pleasant, mellow mushroom taste and smell. It grows sporadically in the summer and beginning of autumn in all woodlands, and is most abundant in deciduous forests of warmer regions. It is a tasty edible species but needs to be cooked well; it is slightly poisonous when raw and may cause digestive problems. It differs from the Bitter Bolete in the red mouth of the tubes and the mild taste of its flesh.

Red-Stemmed Bolete

The Red-Stemmed Bolete is described in detail on the next two pages. The main characteristics in which it differs from the Bitter Bolete are the red mouth of the tubes in the mature fruit bodies and the red scaly stem.

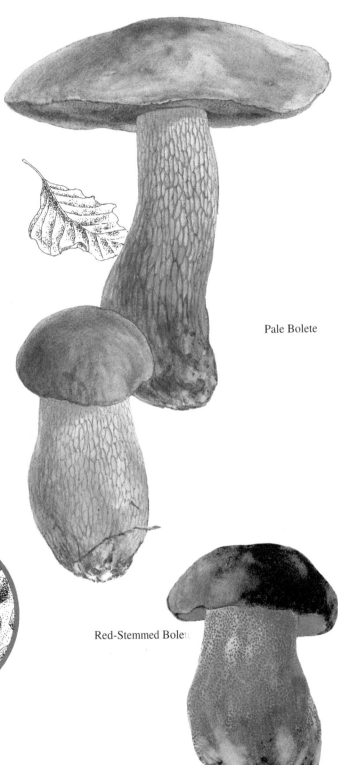

Pale Bolete

Red-Stemmed Bolete

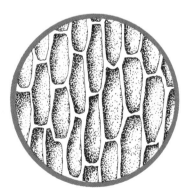

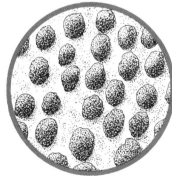

The Pale Bolete has a network with conspicuous red loops.

The Red-Stemmed Bolete has a red scaly stem.

65

☠ Devil's Boletus

Boletus satanas Lenz

The cap is 50 to 230 mm wide, almost spherical when young, later becoming convex and cushion-like flat, whitish, grey-yellow to silvery brown, with a knob on the surface and a subtomentose skin. The tubes are yellow, only 10 to 25 mm long in older mushrooms; they turn blue when cut. The mouth of the tubes is crimson-red and olive with age, becoming a greenish blue when pressed. The stem is beet-shaped and swollen when young, yellow on top with a fine red network, crimson-red in the middle and light ochre at the bottom. The flesh is whitish and turns blue if injured, it does not really change colour when dry. In younger fruit bodies it has a mild spicy smell which later changes into an unpleasant smell like rotting onions. It has a slightly sour nutty taste. It grows sparsely from July to September in limy soils of warmer regions, mostly under hornbeams, oaks and lindens. When raw and not properly cooked it causes constant vomiting and strong pains in the digestive tract. Fatal cases of poisoning have not been recorded as yet. If cooked well, the Devil's Boletus is edible, but as it is rare, it is best left unpicked.

The Devil's Boletus has a red network on its stem.

Red-Stemmed Bolete

Boletus erythropus (Fr. ex Fr.) Pers.

The cap is 50 to 180 mm wide, convex at first, later arched to flat, dark brown to black-brown in colour with a velvet to tomentose surface, dry, bald with age. With age and when pressed it turns a grey black colour. The tubes are yellow at first, later becoming golden yellow and immediately turn blue when touched; the stem is paunchy when young, later cylindrical or club-shaped, yellow under the cap, with red scales on a yellow background in the middle and subtomentose at the base, without a network. The flesh is a rich-yellow colour – when broken or cut it turns an intense blue colour, then fades after a while and remains a grey-yellow colour. It has a pleasant mushroom taste and smell. It grows a lot in the summer and autumn in foothill spruce woods. It is also found in smaller quantities under deciduous trees on the banks of ponds. It is an excellent edible mushroom. It is particularly popular for its firm flesh and strong aroma and is used for making sauces and soups, while the young fruit bodies are pickled in sour brine. It can be safely distinguished from the Devil's Boletus by the darker skin of its cap and the red scales on its stem.

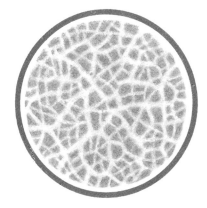

The Red-Stemmed Bolete has a red scaly surface on its stem.

☠ Antabuse Ink Cap

Coprinus atramentarius (Bull. ex Fr.) Fr.

The cap is 30 to 60 mm wide, egg-shaped when young, grey-white, grey or grey-brown, soon becoming bell-shaped, later flat, with lengthwise grooves and brown flakes at the apex. Once the spores ripen, the margin of the cap begins to turn up, and gradually dissolves due to the effect of enzymes and changes into soft 'porridge'. The gills are dense when young, flattened, white at the edges but soon going dark and dissolving into black 'porridge'. The stem can grow up to 200 mm high, is breakable, cylindrical, hollow later on, white, smooth, shiny and root-like. The fruit bodies grow in clusters, often from substrate containing cellulose. The flesh is white, with an indistinctive taste and smell. It grows from May to November in heavily manured sites, pastures, orchards, parks, gardens, compost, woodland paths, ditches, waste ground, dumps and in the middle of housing estates. It is found in abundance in lowlands and foothills. It is classed as a poisonous mushroom because if eaten with alcohol it can cause intensive acetaldehyde poisoning. The symptoms appear 20 minutes to two hours after the consumption of alcohol.

Take care not to drink alcohol when eating food that contains the Antabuse Ink Cap.

Coprinaceae

Shaggy Ink Cap; Lawyer's Wig

Coprinus comatus (Müll. ex Fr.) S.F. Gray

The cap is cylindrical when young, 30 to 60 mm wide and 50 to 100 mm high, later bell-shaped, with coarse scales, white and ochre at the apex. With age, the spores ripen, the margin turns upwards, the flesh and the skin change from a pinkish to a black-violet colour until the entire cap turns into a black soft 'porridge'. The gills are dense when young, free, white, quite high, later turning pink and finally also turning to black 'porridge'. The young fruit bodies have a membranous veil covering the gills; when older, this veil disappears leaving a white ring movable along the stem. The stem is breakable, cylindrical, quite long and often root-like, hollow with age, white, smooth and shiny. The flesh is whitish, with a pleasant taste and smell. It grows from April to November usually in clusters, sometimes on its own on heavily manured sites, in pastures, orchards, parks, gardens and dumps. After rain it is found in abundance in lowlands and foothills. It is an edible mushroom but its use for cooking purposes is limited. It must be processed immediately otherwise the fruit bodies ripen and turn into liquid 'porridge'. It differs from the Antabuse Ink Cap in its scales and the cylindrical shape of its cap.

Food containing the Shaggy Ink Cap/Lawyer's Wig mixed with alcoholic drinks does not cause poisoning.

☠ Little White Inocybe

Inocybe geophylla (Sow. ex Fr.) Kumm.

The cap measures 5 to 30 mm in diameter, it is egg-shaped when young and attached to the stem by a web, soon becoming conical and later broad to flat with a prominent knob. Radial cracks then appear. It is lilac to rich-violet in colour, smooth and silky. The gills are moderately dense, free, whitish at first, later a clay yellow to brown with whitish edges. The stem is thin, broadening out into a bulb at the base, light violet, later growing pale. The flesh is thin, whitish with a violet shade, with an unpleasant taste and a sperm-like smell. It grows from July to October in all woodlands, groves, on the banks of ponds, parks. It grows in numerous clumps and is found in lowlands and highlands. It is a poisonous mushroom and if consumed it may cause muscarine-type poisoning. The presence of muscarine in inocybe mushrooms varies, but is always dangerous, so never prepare any food from these mushrooms. The Little White Inocybe is often confused with smaller violet-coloured boletes, mostly with the Amethyst Deceiver, so take care.

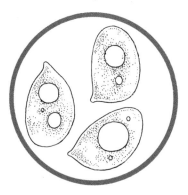

The spores of the Little White Inocybe

Amethyst Deceiver

Laccaria amethystea (Huds. ex Hook.) Cooke

The cap is 20 to 50 mm wide, arched at first, later flat with a depressed hollow in the middle, naked on the surface at first, later becoming velvet to finely flaky, a rich-violet colour when young and becoming pale to ochre with age, with fine grooves on the margin and slightly waved. The gills are 3 to 5 mm high, always violet, dense, often curled and dusty white from the spores. The stem is entirely violet, 30 to 70 mm high, 3 to 5 mm wide, firm, cylindrical, sometimes crooked or flattened, full when young, later becoming tubed and hollow. The flesh is violet when young, later becoming pale with an indistinctive taste and smell. It grows from June to October in deciduous and coniferous woodlands often in numerous clumps. It is an edible mushroom, often used for soups and to add colour to a meal. It preserves its colour even when pickled. However, only the caps should be picked for cooking. The best way to distinguish the Amethyst Deceiver from the Little White Inocybe is by its violet gills (or the microscopic examination of the spores.)

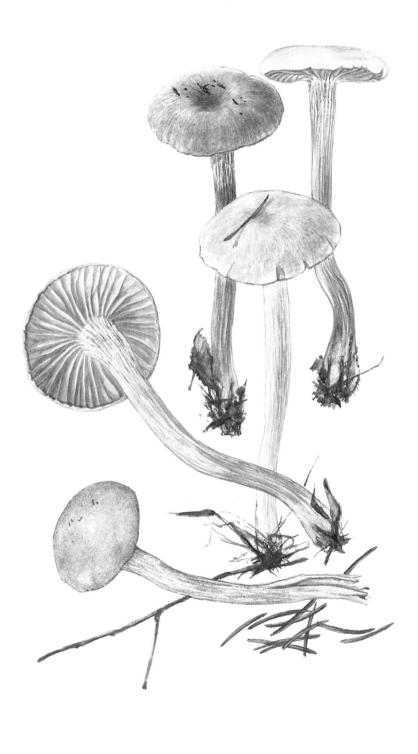

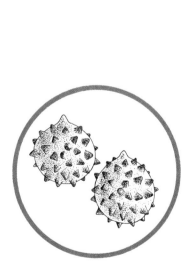

The spores of the Amethyst Deceiver

☠ Clay-Coloured Inocybe

Inocybe argillacea (Pers.) Fay.

The cap is 5 to 30 mm wide, egg-shaped at first, attached to the stem by a web, soon becoming conical, then broadly flat with age with a low knob and radial cracks appearing on its surface. The skin of the cap is fibrillose, silky, white, yellowing at the apex with age. The gills are moderately dense, free, white for a long time, turning brown with age and whitish with a fringe at the edges. The stem is thin, broadening out slightly into a bulb at the base, silky and white. The flesh is thin, white, with an unpleasant taste and sperm-like smell. It grows from July to October in all kinds of woodlands, groves, parks, on the banks of ponds, in cemeteries and gardens. Some experts consider this species to be the white form of the Little White Inocybe. It is a poisonous mushroom with a relatively high content of muscarine. The poisoning is similar to that of the Blushing Inocybe (see page 30). The Clay-Coloured Inocybe has been confused many times with certain edible mushrooms, including the Miller/Plum Agaric/Sweetbread Mushroom or the Fairy-Ring Champignon.

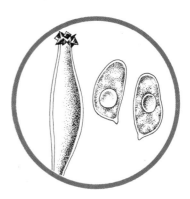

The cystidia and spores of the Clay-Coloured Inocybe

Miller; Plum Agaric; Sweetbread Mushroom

Clitopilus prunulus (Scop. ex Fr.) Kumm.

Fairy-Ring Champignon

Marasmius oreades (Bolt. ex Fr.) Fr.

Miller; Plum Agaric; Sweetbread Mushroom

A detailed description of the Miller/Plum Agaric/Sweetbread Mushroom is found on page 157. It differs from the Clay-Coloured Inocybe above all in its short cylindrical stem, and considerably decurrent gills, which become fleshy pink when older.

Fairy-Ring Champignon

The cap is 15 to 35 mm wide, bluntly conical or convex at first, later becoming broadly flat with a blunt knob in the middle; smooth, very moist, tan or light flesh-coloured, darker when moist. The gills are very dense, thick, high, sinuately attached at the stem, and somewhat lighter than the surface of the cap. The stem is cylindrical, long, thin, full, light ochre, white tomentose at the bottom, flexible even unbreakable. The flesh is whitish, very thin, with a pleasant taste and intensive bitter almond smell. It grows from May to October in grassy areas, woodlands, gardens and parks, in lowlands and mountains. It is an excellent edible mushroom and suitable for soups. Only the caps are picked for cooking. It differs from the Clay-Coloured Inocybe in its flexible stem and bitter almond smell.

Miller; Plum Agaric;
Sweetbread Mushroom

Fairy-Ring Champignon

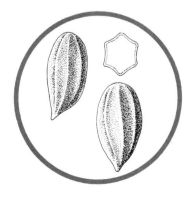

The spores of the Miller/Plum
Agaric/Sweetbread Mushroom

The spores of the
Fairy-Ring Champignon

☠ Torn Inocybe

Inocybe lacera (Fr.) Kumm.

The cap measures 20 to 30 mm in diameter. At first it is covered with a brown or brown-ochre down. It is conical, soon becoming broadly arched and sometimes with a small knob; the margin is silky, often torn. Radial cracks appear on its surface with age. The skin is dry, flattened and tomentose at first, with protruding scales soon appearing from the apex, grey-brown to brown with a translucently yellow-brown under-skin layer. The gills are quite dense, free, whitish when young, later browning with a fleshy shade and whitish edges. The stem is erect, relatively thin, fibrous, slightly thicker at the base, grey-brown, white for a long time at the top with fine brownish fibres. The flesh is thin, whitish, brownish at the stem, with an indistinctive, even unpleasant, taste and sperm-like smell. It grows abundantly from July to October in coniferous woodlands, pine woods, along paths, on the banks of ponds, woodland borders and recultivated dumps. It is mostly found in pine woods on sandy soil in lowlands and highlands. It is a poisonous mushroom with a high content of muscarine. Although it is an inconspicuous mushroom and does not attract much attention, it is occasionally confused with the Fairy-Ring Champignon, laccarias or other small species.

A cross-section of the Torn Inocybe

Fairy-Ring Champignon

Marasmius oreades (Bolt. ex Fr.) Fr.

A detailed description of the Fairy-Ring Champignon is given on pages 33 and 73. To distinguish it from the inocybe mushrooms, note the following: the Fairy-Ring Champignon has very sparse gills, a flexible unbreakable stem and an intense bitter almond smell. The Torn Inocybe has dense gills, a fragile stem, a sperm-like smell and the surface of its cap is tomentose.

A cross-section of the fruit bodies of the Fairy-Ring Champignon (notice the sparse gills).

☠ Turnip Inocybe

Inocybe napipes J. Lange

The cap measures 30 to 50 mm in diameter, is conical at first, later becoming broadly conical with a permanently sharp knob. The skin is bald at first or very finely fibrous, but soon becomes radially fibrous, dark brown to black-brown at the apex of the cap. The gills are quite dense, sinuately attached to the stem, whitish, greyish to light-brown in old age. The stem is cylindrical, thin, erect, broadening out at the base into a small turnip-like bulb, finely fibrous with long stripes, hoary at the top, whitish brown and whitish on the bulb. The flesh is whitish to light brown in colour, with an indistinctive taste and a mild sperm-like smell. It grows at the end of summer and in the autumn in mossy spruce and pine woods or birch woods. The fruit bodies appear in small clumps. It is quite a poisonous species with a high content of muscarine. It is just as dangerous as the Blushing Inocybe (see page 30). The presence of poisonous substances does not change even with cooking or the drying out of the fruit bodies. The Turnip Inocybe is sometimes confused with the Fairy-Ring Champignon.

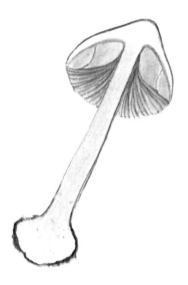

A cross-section of the Turnip Inocybe

Fairy-Ring Champignon

Marasmius oreades (Bolt. ex Fr.) Fr.

A detailed description of the Fairy-Ring Champignon is found on pages 33 and 73. It grows abundantly from May to October in rings or numerous clumps in meadows, pastures, grassy woodlands from lowlands to mountains. It is an excellent edible mushroom, but only the caps are used for cooking. It can be easily distinguished from the Turnip Inocybe because it has a flexible, very tough unbreakable stem, sparse gills and, above all, a pleasant bitter almond smell.

A cross-section of the fruit body of the Fairy-Ring Champignon (apart from the sparse gills it can also be distinguished by its flexible stem and pleasant bitter almond smell).

☠ Sulphur Tuft

Hypholoma fasciculare (Huds. ex Fr.) Kumm.

The cap is 20 to 50 mm wide, bell-shaped when young, later arched to flat with a low rounded knob, sulphur yellow in colour, but becoming orange to rusty-brown in the middle, smooth, naked, with a shiny skin when moist. The gills are dense and roundly attached to the stem, sulphur-yellow at first, becoming a dirty-green and black-violet with age. In youth they are covered with a webbed veil which disappears in old age leaving only a small fringe on the margin of the cap and small remains on the stem in the shape of a disappearing fibrous ring. The stem is cylindrical, slender, erect or slightly crooked, hollow when old, smooth, naked, sulphur-yellow becoming brown at the base. The flesh is yellow, brownish at the base of the stem, with an earthy smell and disgusting bitter taste. It grows from March to December in rich clusters on rotting stumps and on the roots of deciduous and coniferous trees. It grows in masses in lowlands and mountainous areas. It is considered inedible because of its terrible bitter taste. However, there are reports that it can cause similar poisoning to that of the Death Cap. Several cases of fatal poisonings have been recorded.

The gills of the Sulphur Tuft are sulphur-yellow at first, then dirty-green.

Tufted Yellow Agaric; Conifer Tuft

Hypholoma capnoides (Fr. ex Fr.) Kumm.

The cap measures 20 to 50 mm in diameter, it has thin flesh, is convex when young, later broadly flat, yellowish or ochre-brown, dry, smooth with remains of a veil on the sharp margin. The gills are dense, moderately wide, rounded at the stem, whitish when young, later a poppy-seed blue-grey colour becoming violet-brown with age. The gills are covered with a webbed yellowish veil which disappears with age. The stem is slender, cylindrical, often crooked or twisted, and like the Sulphur Tuft pushes up through the substrate or cluster of mushrooms into the light. It is whitish at the top, with a silky lustre, full, later hollow, brownish at the base, fibrously flattened with remains of a ring on the upper part of the stem when young. The flesh is whitish or light-yellow, fragile and juicy, indistinctive, with a slightly musty smell and very pleasant mushroom nutty taste. It grows abundantly in the autumn (in spring it appears sporadically) in entire clusters in coniferous woodlands mostly from the stumps and dead roots of spruces. It is found in lowlands and in mountain areas where it grows most abundantly in the cooler season. It is a good edible mushroom. It can be easily distinguished from the Sulphur Tuft by the blue-grey colouring of the gills.

The gills of the Tufted Yellow Agaric/Conifer Tuft are whitish at first, then blue-grey.

☠ Yellowish Lactarius

Lactarius helvus (Fr.) Fr.

The cap is 50 to 120 mm wide, broadly arched at first, later becoming flat with a paunchy depression in the middle, ochre-brown, with flaky flattened scales, dry, inrolled when young, fragile. The gills are 3 to 5 mm high, moderately dense, yellow-ochre, decurrent at the stem. The stem is cylindrical, 40 to 120 mm high, 5 to 25 mm wide, the same colour as the cap or slightly paler, white tomentose at the base under the mycelium, hollow when older. The flesh is light ochre, often red-brown at the base of the stem, turning fleshy red when injured; it is hard and brittle when young, becoming crumbly with age. When cut it releases a transparent watery milk of a slightly bitter taste. The young fruit bodies have a pleasant fruity smell; maturing and drying out fruit bodies smell like chicory or spicy soup. It grows abundantly from July to October in damp coniferous woodlands. The fruit bodies appear in large clumps, often in acid soil and peat-moss. It is inedible and moderately poisonous. Vomiting and diarrhoea appear in most people about one to four hours after the consumption of several fruit bodies.

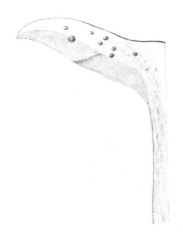

A cross-section of part of the fruit body of the Yellowish Lactarius

Orange-Brown Lactarius;
Weeping Milk Cap; Bradley

Lactarius volemus (Fr.) Fr.

The cap measures 50 to 150 mm in diameter, is arched with an inrolled margin when young, later flat, slightly depressed in the middle, fleshy, tough, fragile, red-brown or orange, dry when older and slightly cracked. The gills are 4 to 7 mm high, dense, whitish to creamy, becoming rusty-brown with age, decurrent at the stem. The stem is cylindrical, 60 to 110 mm long, 15 to 20 mm wide, full, smooth, without a ring, light red-brown or orange. The flesh is brittle, hard, whitish, and when cut releases lots of white sweet milk which leaves brownish stains when it dries. It has a sweetish taste and a pleasant smell. Older smell like fish. It grows in summer and autumn in all woodlands, particularly pine woods mixed with birches. The fruit bodies usually appear on their own, rarely in clumps. When the Orange-Brown Lactarius/Weeping Milk Cap/Bradley appears then it means there is a decline in moisture in woodlands so that other species of mushrooms stop growing. It is an excellent edible mushroom which can be eaten raw. It differs from the Yellowish Lactarius mainly in the amount of sweet milk it releases and the smooth surface of the cap.

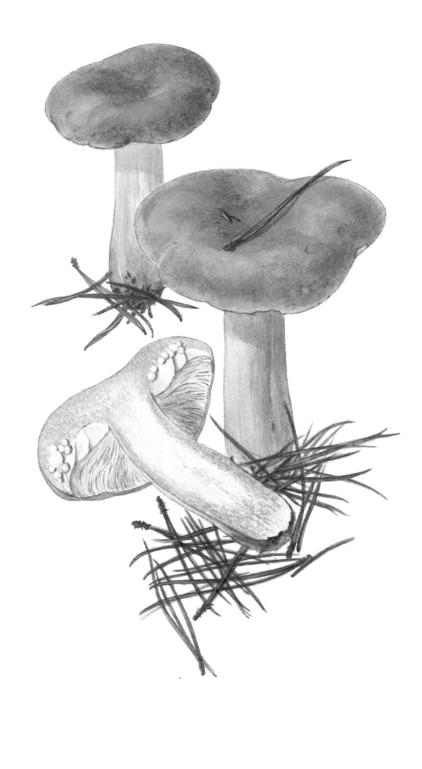

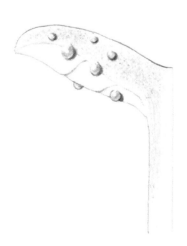

A cross-section of the fruit body of the Orange-Brown Luctarius/Weeping Milk Cap/Bradley (notice the amount of white milk released).

☠ Woolly Milk Cap; Woolly Lactarius; Bearded Milk Cap

Lactarius torminosus (Schaeff. ex Fr.) S.F. Gray

The cap is 50 to 120 mm wide, arched when young, conspicuously inrolled, highly fibrillose at the margin, fleshy-pink or reddish with several concentrated, lighter-coloured rings. The middle of the cap has a paunchy depression when young and becomes slightly funnel-shaped in old age. The gills are 3 to 4 mm high, dense, creamy-pinkish, decurrent at the stem. The stem is cylindrical, hard, fragile, hollow, pale to slightly pinkish, 30 to 70 mm high, 10 to 25 mm wide. The flesh is whitish, pinkish under the skin of the cap and stem; it releases a white milk. It stings when tasted but has an indistinctive smell. It grows in summer and particularly in the autumn in light woodlands under birches in large quantities. It prefers acid soils and is found under birches even outside woodlands. The milk contains poisonous substances making the mushroom unsuitable for cooking. It causes diarrhoea and vomiting.

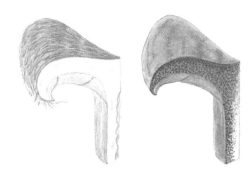

A cross-section of part of the fruit body of the Woolly Milk Cap/Woolly Lactarius/Bearded Milk Cap (left) and the Spruce Milk Cap (right)

Spruce Milk Cap
Lactarius deterrimus Gröger

Saffron Milk Cap; Milky Agaric; Delicious Milk Cap
Lactarius deliciosus (L. ex Fr.) S.F. Gray

Orange-Brown Lactarius; Weeping Milk Cap; Bradley
Lactarius volemus (Fr.) Fr.

Spruce Milk Cap

The cap is 30 to 80 mm wide, arched with an inrolled margin at first, later flat, depressed in the middle, funnel-shaped with a sharp margin with age, fleshy or orange-red in colour with darker concentrated rings and green stains with age. The gills are dense, fragile, decurrent at the stem, red-orange, turning green when injured. The stem is cylindrical, short, fragile, soon hollow, red-orange with green stains. The flesh is whitish, in places saturated with orange milk, turning green when injured. It has a sharp, herbal taste and a pleasant smell. It grows abundantly from August to October in spruce thickets and on the borders of grassy areas of woodlands on higher ground. It differs from the Woolly Milk Cap/Woolly Lactarius/Bearded Milk Cap in its carrot-red milk.

Saffron Milk Cap; Milky Agaric; Delicious Milk Cap

It is very similar to the Spruce Milk Cap but is bigger and more fleshy. The cap measures up to 150 mm in width and has distinctive rings. It grows under pines. A detailed description is found on page 111. It differs from the Woolly Milk Cap/Woolly Lactarius/Bearded Milk Cap in its carrot-red milk.

Orange-Brown Lactarius; Weeping Milk Cap; Bradley

A detailed description is found on page 81. It can be easily distinguished from the Woolly Milk Cap/Woolly Lactarius/Bearded Milk Cap by its sweet, white heavily flowing milk.

Spruce Milk Cap

Saffron Milk Cap; Milky Agaric; Delicious Milk Cap

Orange-Brown Lactarius; Weeping Milk Cap; Bradley

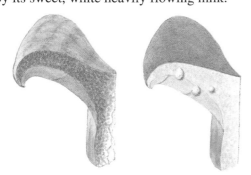

A cross-section of part of the fruit body of the Saffron Milk Cap/ Milky Agaric/Delicious Milk Cap (left) and of the Orange-Brown Lactarius/Weeping Milk Cap/Bradley (right)

☠ Jack-O-Lantern

Omphalotus olearius (D.C. ex Fr.) Sing.

The cap measures 40 to 110 mm in diameter, is arched with an inrolled margin when young, becoming broadly flat with a funnel-shaped depression in the middle and with a folded sharp margin; it has orange fibres on a yellow-orange background, darker to chestnut brown in colour in the middle with ingrown scales at first, later becoming naked, dry and with a silky lustre. The gills are 2 to 6 mm high, dense, undivided at the edges, flexible, deeply decurrent at the stem when older; golden yellow when young, later orange. In the dark they sometimes have a blue-green shine. The stem is 40 to 120 mm long, 7 to 30 mm wide, full, thicker under the cap and becoming narrower towards the bottom, subtomentose on the surface, matt, yellow-orange or yellow-ochre in colour. The flesh is finely fibrous, quite tough, dry, flexible, yellowish with a pink shade (it tends to be whitish in colour in the cap), of an indistinctive taste and smell. It grows from July to November in warmer regions, usually in rich clusters on stumps and trunks of deciduous trees or near them. It is often found growing wildly on fruit trees. It is a poisonous mushroom whose toxins have not been examined as yet. Symptoms of light poisoning appear one to two hours after consumption.

The Jack-O-Lantern usually grows on wood.

Funnel Cap 🍴

Clitocybe gibba (Pers. ex Fr.) Kumm.

Chanterelle 🍴

Cantharellus cibarius Fr. ex Fr.

Funnel Cap

The cap is 30 to 80 mm wide, arched when young, soon becoming flat, depressed, funnel-shaped with a small knob on the bottom of the depression, with thin flesh, smooth, ochre-yellow to red-brown, growing pale, with folds on the margin. The gills are dense, low, decurrent far down the stem, almost white at first, later becoming creamy. The stem is cylindrical, smooth, naked, full, whitish or light ochre and tomentose at the base. The flesh is white, of an indistinctive but pleasant taste and with a pleasant mushroom smell. It grows in clusters from July to October in all types of woodland, in moss next to paths and in woodland meadows. It is a very good edible mushroom. It needs to be cooked for a long time. It can be easily distinguished from the poisonous Jack-O-Lantern according to the place of growth, as it never grows on wood.

Chanterelle

The cap is 20 to 70 mm wide, arched when young, later becoming broadly arched with a margin that is inrolled for a long time, and finally funnel-shaped with a curved and lobed margin. It has a yolk-yellow colour, growing pale, and is naked and matt with thin flesh. The Chanterelle has no real gills but only interconnected low blunt-like folds, decurrent far down the stem, crisplike and the same colour as the cap. The stem is cylindrical, narrowing off at the bottom, full, yellow, smooth, naked; it grows brown when pressed. The flesh is whitish, slightly yellowish, with a slightly stinging taste and a pleasant spicy smell. It grows from June to October in deciduous and coniferous woodland. Apart from the Jack-O-Lantern it cannot be mistaken for any other poisonous species. Note: the Jack-O-Lantern usually grows in clusters from wood whereas the Chanterelle grows out of the ground.

Funnel Cap

Chanterelle

☠ Yellow Coral Mushroom

Ramaria aurea (Schaeff. ex Fr.) Quél.

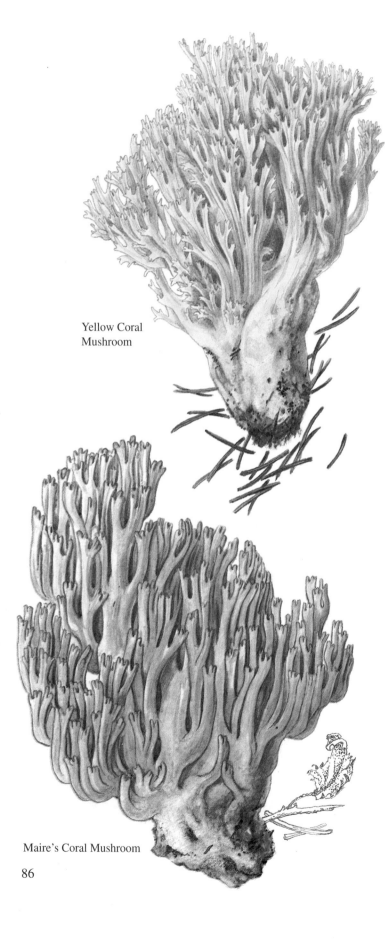

Yellow Coral
Mushroom

Maire's Coral Mushroom

The fruit body is bushy, irregularly spherical, measuring 60 to 120 mm in diameter. The large, fleshy, naked and whitish stem branches out into multiple rounded, ungrooved, very short, dense, cauliflower-like clustered twigs. In youth the twigs are honey to chrome-yellow or golden yellow in colour, in adulthood ochre-yellow, ending in several small golden yellow conical teeth. The flesh is whitish inside, yellowish beneath the surface, soft, with an indistinctive taste and smell. The Yellow Coral Mushroom grows from July to September in deciduous and, to a lesser extent, also in coniferous woodlands in lowlands and highlands where it grows in abundance. The fruit bodies grow in small clumps. It is moderately poisonous, containing the fairly strong laxative emodine that irritates the mucous membrane of the large intestine. Maire's Coral Mushroom (*Ramaria mairei*) which grows sparsely in summer and the beginning of autumn in coniferous and deciduous woodlands also contains the same poison. In youth the twigs are pink-violet, in old age creamy to light-ochre. The flesh is whitish inside, yellowish beneath the surface, soft sweetish at first, later becoming bitter in taste with an indistinctive smell.

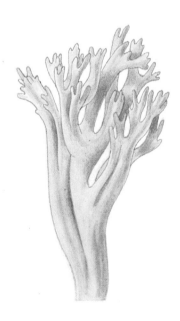

The Yellow Coral Mushroom has bushy twigs.

Crisped Sparassis; Cauliflower Mushroom

Sparassis crispa (Wulf.) ex Fr.

The fruit body is irregularly spherical, 100 to 400 mm wide, whitish, creamy or ochre-coloured, composed of multiple flat, clustered, leafy ended, very curly and serrated twigs growing out of a thick stem buried in the ground. The gilled curly twigs have a fertile hymenium on both sides. The flesh is whitish, flexible, waxy, of a strong spicy smell with a touch of aniseed and a slightly stinging, nutty sweetish taste. It grows from July to October in coniferous woodlands, most often at the base of a pine or larch tree trunks. It is found most often in pine woods in sandy soils. From a distance it resembles a wash sponge. It is one of the best edible mushrooms and is often sold at markets. Because of its content of antibiotic substances and tough flesh, the Crisped Sparassis/Cauliflower Mushroom can be stored for a long time in a damp, cold cellar, placed in a bowl of water. It can be easily distinguished from the coral mushrooms because of the leafy spread of the twig ends.

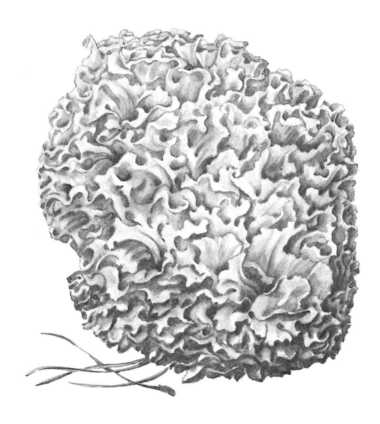

The Crisped Sparassis/Cauliflower Mushroom has twigs which branch out into leaf-like forms.

A cross-section of the fruit body of the Crisped Sparassis/Cauliflower Mushroom

☠ Beautiful Clavaria; Pinkish Coral Mushroom

Ramaria formosa (Pers. ex Fr.) Quél.

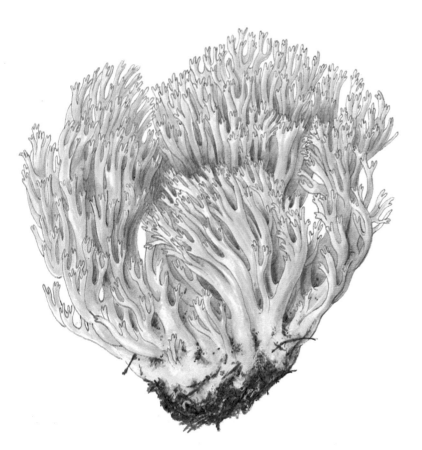

Unlike other species of Ramaria, the fruit body is more robust, richly branched, bush-like, growing to a height of 200 mm and 150 mm wide. The stem part of the fruit body is fleshy, 20 to 30 mm wide, partially buried in the ground with a naked light-ochre or pinkish surface. It is short, sometimes elongated or branched and reaching as far as the neighbouring clusters. It has rich upward branches ending in fork-like or serrated twigs. The surface of the branches is usually smooth, sometimes wrinkled in places. The bottom parts of the branches are light salmon-pink, fleshy or yellow-ochre and the ends tend to be lemon-yellow at first. After the ripening of the spores, the entire fruit body turns a light-ochre colour. The flesh is pinkish when young, white when older and reddens when wounded, with an unpleasant bitter taste and indistinctive smell. The fruit bodies are found in abundance in the summer and autumn particularly in deciduous woodlands. Normally they grow in clumps. The Beautiful Clavaria/Pinkish Coral Mushroom is widespread throughout the temperate zone of the Northern hemisphere. It is a poisonous species because it contains emodine which irritates the mucous membrane of the large intestine and causes strong diarrhoea.

The Beautiful Clavaria/Pinkish Coral Mushroom has bush-like twigs.

Crisped Sparassis; Cauliflower Mushroom
Sparassis crispa (Wulf.) ex Fr.

Elegant Coral Fungus
Polyporus umbellatus (Pers.) ex Fr.

Crisped Sparassis;
Cauliflower Mushroom

Crisped Sparassis; Cauliflower Mushroom

An irregular spherical fruit body growing to a width of 400 mm and weighing several kilogrammes. It resembles a bath sponge in appearance. A detailed description is found on the previous page. It is common in deciduous woodlands, growing mainly at the trunks of pines and larches. It differs from *Ramaria* in size and the leafy flat ended twigs.

Elegant Coral Fungus

The entire fruit body resembles the head of a young ram and in some regions it is popularly called 'ram's head'. The spherical fruit body can grow to a width of 400 mm. The thick stem has multiple twigs in a large number of stumps ending in small caps. One cluster may contain some 250 such small caps measuring 15 to 40 mm. Their surface is covered in fine scales, grey or ochre in colour and depressed in the middle. The underside of the caps have white tubes with a small mouth growing far down the stem. The white flesh is juicy, fleshy, with a mellow dill-like smell with a very pleasant, delicious taste resembling nuts. The fruit body grows from a black underground sclerotia mainly in deciduous woodlands. The Elegant Coral Fungus is widespread throughout the temperate zone of the Northern hemisphere. It is easy to distinguish from the *Ramaria* by its cap-like ended twigs.

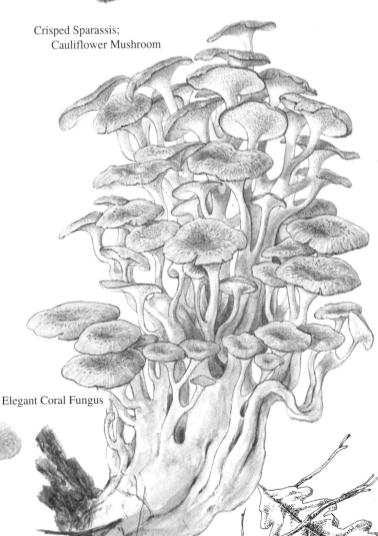

Elegant Coral Fungus

The twigs of the Elegant
Coral Fungus end in small caps.

☠ Sickener

Russula emetica (Schaeff. ex Fr.) S.F. Gray

The cap is 40 to 100 mm in diameter, convex when young, soon becoming arched to flat, slightly depressed, blood red, turning very pale after rain, bald, smooth, greasy and shiny, viscid in the rain with easy-to-peel skin. The gills are dense, free, rounded at the stem, pure white when young, later yellowing. The stem is cylindrical, fragile, pure white, in rare cases reddish resembling cotton wool with age. The flesh is white and only red beneath the skin, with a strong burning taste and pleasant fruity smell. It grows from July to October in all shady woodlands. It can be found in great abundance in coniferous marshlands with deep moss. It is one of the most beautifully coloured mushrooms. However its considerable resin content makes it a dangerous mushroom. It is particularly poisonous if not cooked properly and causes persistent stomach problems and heavy vomiting, hence its name.

The spore dust of the Sickener

Marshy Russula

Russula paludosa Britz.

The cap is 50 to 150 mm wide, convex in youth, soon becoming flat, depressed, wild rose or strawberry-red, turning pale, smooth, viscid and two-thirds of the skin can be peeled. The gills are dense, free, quite high, whitish at first, later creamy and slightly reddish at the edges. The stem is cylindrical, up to 30 mm wide, white, often lightly-reddish, soon becoming like cotton wool inside. The flesh is white, fine, fragile, with a burning taste in young fruit bodies and a pleasant one in older fruit bodies and an indistinctive smell. It grows from July to September in damp coniferous woodlands in lowlands and highlands. In sandy pine woods it can be found growing in heather, moss and among bilberries in great abundance. It also grows a lot in peat-moss. It is an excellent edible mushroom and versatile for cooking. Unfortunately it resembles some 20 other species of red russulas. It differs from the Sickener in the colour of its gills, spore dust and taste. The Sickener always has a strong burning taste and is usually smaller. The spore dust of the Marshy Russula is light-ochre in colour and this is also reflected in the colour of the gills (if in doubt let the spore dust fall out onto paper).

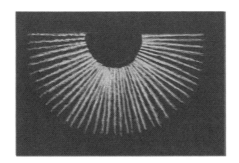

The spore dust of the Marshy Russula

☠ Verrucose Earth Ball

Scleroderma verrucosum (Bull. ex Pers.)

The ground fruit body is irregularly spherical, 20 to 50 mm wide, narrowing off at the bottom. The peridium (the wall of the fruit body of Gasteromycetes) is very thin, flexible, yellow-ochre or yellow-brown, always darker at the apex, with fine amber-brown shelf-like cracks often appearing, resembling papillae. The spore (spore-bearing part of the fruit body) is tough when young, white, later black-blue to dark-violet, with a pleasant, strong mushroom taste and spicy smell; it gradually dries out and changes into a crumbly grey-black substance which breaks up into grey-brown spore dust. It grows quite abundantly from July to September in deciduous and mixed woodlands, avenues, parks, along woodland paths and mainly in sandy ground. The Verrucose Earth Ball is a dangerous mushroom. The young fruit body (thoroughly dried) can be used only in limited amounts as a food spice. Ripened fruit bodies with a firm, dark inside cause persistent vomiting, drowsiness, blurred vision, sweating, painful diarrhoea, headaches, breathing problems and hot sensations in one to two hours after consumption. The poison of the Verrucose Earth Ball is particularly dangerous for people with heart disease.

A cross-section of the Verrucose Earth Ball

Dead Man's Foot 🍴

Pisolithus arrhizus (Scop. ex Pers.) Rausch.

Pestle Puffball 🍴

Calvatia excipuliformis (Scop. ex Pers.) Perd.

Dead Man's Foot

The underground irregular spherical fruit body is 30 to 150 mm wide, heavy and hard. When older it grows above the ground surface and disperses gradually. There is a small 'root' or, on the contrary, a robust developed cylindrical root-branched sterile base at the bottom of the fruit body. The peridium is thin, smooth, ochre-yellow, later turning dark-brown and when ripe breaks up into scales. The spore mass is composed of tiny round or many-sided pips, yellow when young in a black sterile network, later turning brown and breaking up into spore dust. It has a pleasant taste and strong mushroom smell. It grows from July to September in light, mainly pine woods on sandy and sunny sites. In some places it grows in abundance. The young fruit bodies are edible, but in small amounts only, and are used as spices

Pestle Puffball

The club-shaped fruit body is 50 to 150 mm high, 30 to 80 mm wide, white when young, later turning ochre to light brown. The sterile stem part is usually robust, cylindrical, narrowing off or, on the contrary, club-shaped at the bottom. The peridium is grainy and bristly with shelf-like cracks appearing, whitish, and breaks up into pieces. The spore mass is white, soft with a delicious taste and mushroom smell at first. It turns olive-brown in colour when it ripens and becomes soft and watery then eventually dries up, turns brown and breaks up into pieces. It grows abundantly in the summer and autumn in woodland meadows and deciduous and coniferous woodlands. The young fruit bodies that are still white when cut are suitable for cooking and taste excellent.

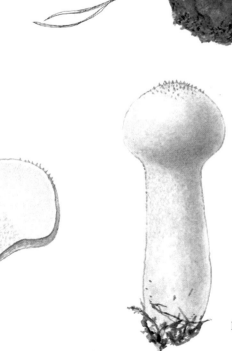

Dead Man's Foot

A cross-section of the Pestle Puffball

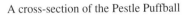

Pestle Puffball

☠ Earth Ball

Scleroderma citrinum Pers.

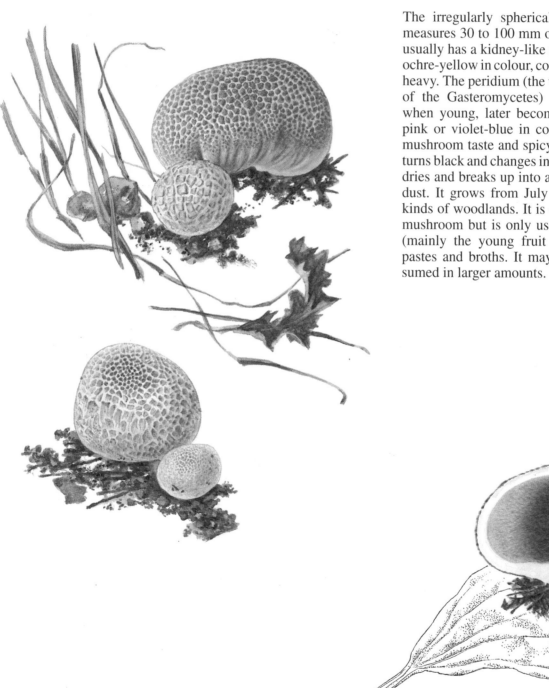

The irregularly spherical ground fruit body measures 30 to 100 mm on its longer side and usually has a kidney-like section. It is straw to ochre-yellow in colour, conspicuously hard and heavy. The peridium (the wall of the fruit body of the Gasteromycetes) is white and tough when young, later becoming pinkish, violet-pink or violet-blue in colour with a pleasant mushroom taste and spicy smell; eventually it turns black and changes into a 'porridge' which dries and breaks up into a greyish green spore dust. It grows from July to November in all kinds of woodlands. It is considered an edible mushroom but is only used in small amounts (mainly the young fruit bodies) for spicing pastes and broths. It may be harmful if consumed in larger amounts.

A cross-section of the fruit body of the Earth Ball

Lycoperdaceae	**Common Puffball; Warted Puffball; Gemmed Puffball**	♉
	Lycoperdon perlatum Pers. ex Pers.	

Lycoperdaceae	**Tumbling Puffball; Tumble Ball**	♉
	Bovista plumbea Pers. ex Pers.	

Tuberaceae	**European Truffle**	♉
	Tuber aestivum Vitt.	

Common Puffball; Warted Puffball; Gemmed Puffball

The fruit bodies are usually pear-shaped, 40 to 80 mm high. The spore mass is spherical with a knob at the apex. When young the entire fruit body is white and covered with small conical papillae. With age the fruit body turns an ochre-brown and then a brown colour. The young spore mass is white and flexible, and when the spores ripen, they turn yellow and grow soft. After the spores ripen, the inside of the spore mass turns into an olive-brown dust. An opening appears at the apex of the fruit body though which the spores pass and then scatter into the surrounding areas. It grows abundantly from June to October in woodlands, pastureland and groves. It is one of the tastiest of mushrooms. Pick only the young fruit bodies which are pure white inside.

Tumbling Puffball; Tumble Ball

The fruit body is 10 to 30 mm wide, grows at ground level, and is sessile. The outer peridium is white but soon begins to peel in bits. The inner peridium is paper-like, grey or blue-grey and a small opening appears at the apex through which the spores pass and scatter. It grows in the summer and autumn in dry grasses along paths, on pasturelands and along woodland paths. It is very tasty mushroom when young.

European Truffle

The fruit body is 20 to 70 mm wide, grows at ground level, and is bulbous, blue-black or black-brown in colour, firm, and densely cracked on the surface into large conical papillae. The flesh is whitish to yellowish when young, later brownish with whitish veins. It grows rarely from July to September on limestone ground under oaks, beeches or hornbeams. It is a very tasty mushroom used as a cooking spice.

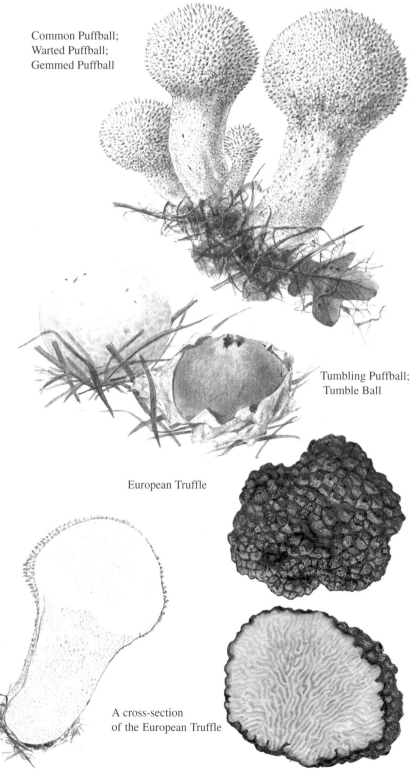

Common Puffball;
Warted Puffball;
Gemmed Puffball

Tumbling Puffball;
Tumble Ball

European Truffle

A cross-section of the Common
Puffball/Warted Puffball/
Gemmed Puffball

A cross-section
of the Tumbling Puffball/
Tumble Ball

A cross-section
of the European Truffle

☠ # Rose Mycena

Mycena rosea (Bull.) Sacc. et Dalla Costa

The cap is 30 to 60 mm wide, conical when young, soon becoming broadly flat, rounded and hunched to flat with a knob in the middle, fragile with thin flesh, with a watery transparent look, light-pink, no violet tint, with a skin that is darker when moist and smooth, shiny and bald when dry. The gills are high, sparse, sinuate and decurrent, serrated at the edges, whitish or light pink. The stem is cylindrical, fibrous, hollow, fragile, usually slightly curved at the base, gradually becoming thicker towards the bottom, whitish or light pink, yellowish at the base. The flesh is fragile, whitish or pale pinkish, with a distinctive radish-like taste and smell. It is scattered in growth from July to October solely under deciduous trees. It is easily confused with laccarias or the Fairy-Ring Champignon. The Rose Mycena has a muscarine type of poison, causing salivation, vomiting, diarrhoea, cold shivers and heart problems.

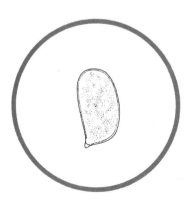

The spores of the Rose Mycena

Deceiver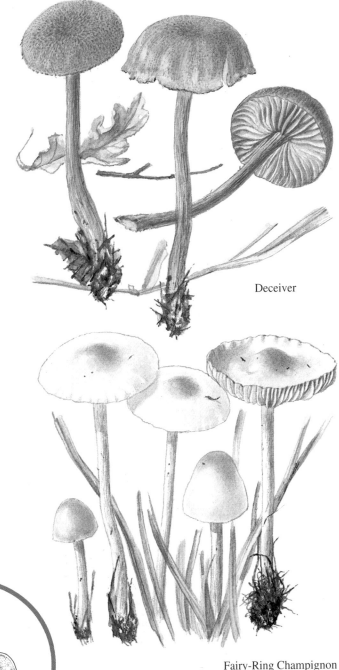
Laccaria laccata (Scop. ex Fr.) Cooke

Fairy-Ring Champignon
Marasmius oreades (Bolt. ex Fr.) Fr.

Deceiver

The cap is 20 to 50 mm wide, bell-shaped when young, later flat, slightly arched, depressed in the middle, a fleshy red or red-brown colour, turn-ing pale, with a finely grooved margin, smooth on the surface, with tiny flakes appear-ing later, thin-fleshed and transparent. The gills are sparse, high, attached to the stem or slightly decurrent, often curved, a pale fleshy-red colour, covered in white spore dust when older, as though varnished. The stem is cylindrical, tough, fibrous becoming cotton wool-like in old age, of a fleshy red colour with an evident white mycelium at the base. The flesh is a light fleshy-red colour, watery, with a mellow or indistinctive taste and smell. It grows profusely from June to October in all types of woodland. It is a good edible mushroom. Only the caps are eaten. It can be distinguished from the Rose Mycena by its red-brown coloured fruit bodies, taste, smell and spores. The spores of the Rose Mycena are smooth while those of the Deceiver are clearly bristly.

Fairy-Ring Champignon

A detailed description of the Fairy-Ring Champignon is found on pages 33 and 73. The Fairy-Ring Champignon is an excellent edible mushroom. Only the caps are eaten. It is easy to distinguish from the Rose Mycena by its unbreakable stem and bitter almond smell.

Deceiver

Fairy-Ring Champignon

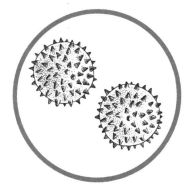

The spores of the Deceiver

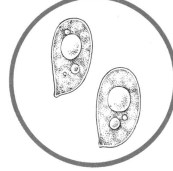

The spores of the Fairy-Ring Champignon

☠ Amethyst Agaric; Lilac Mycena

Mycena pura (Pers. ex Fr.) Kumm.

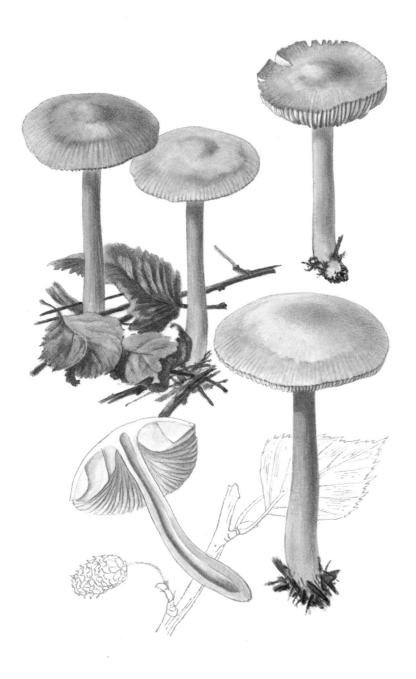

The cap is 20 to 40 mm wide, conical when young, later broadly arched to flat with a knob in the middle, pink-violet or blue-violet in colour, naked, watery and transparent, thin-fleshed, shiny when dry, darker when moist particularly in the middle. Gills are transparent, high, sinuate and decurrent at the stem and serrated at the edges, paunchy, whitish or light-violet in colour. The stem is erect, thin, fibrous, hollow, brittle, dusty at the top, a delicate violet colour. The flesh is thin, fragile, brittle, light violet, with a strong smell and taste of radishes. It grows from July to November in all woodlands in lowlands and high up in mountainous areas, even above the forest border. It is one of the most common mushrooms found in the temperate zone. It is moderately poisonous containing indulin substances which cause hallucination. However this occurs only if a large amount of mushrooms are consumed. Nevertheless, be careful when picking the Amethyst Agaric/Lilac Mycena because it can cause more serious problems in sensitive people.

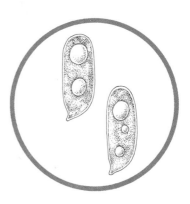

The spores of the Amethyst Agaric/Lilac Mycena

Amethyst Deceiver

Laccaria amethystea (Huds. ex Hook.) Cooke

The cap is 20 to 50 mm wide, arched when young, later flat with a hollow-like depression in the middle. The surface is naked at first, later becoming velvety and even covered with fine flakes, a rich-violet colour when young, turning pale to ochre in old age, with fine grooves at the slightly wavy margin. The gills are 3 to 7 mm high, always violet, sparse, often curled and covered in white spore dust. The stem is all violet, 30 to 70 mm high, 3 to 5 mm wide, firm, cylindrical, sometimes crooked and squashed, full when young, later with hollow tubes. The flesh is pale violet when young, later turning into various shades of violet, tough at the stem, with an indistinctive taste and smell. It grows from June to October in deciduous and coniferous woodlands often in large clumps. It is an edible mushroom, good for flavouring soups, and adds colour to meals. It retains its violet colour even when pickled. Only use the caps for cooking. It can easily be distinguished from the Amethyst Agaric/Lilac Mycena by its taste and smell. There is no strong radish-like smell and taste and its gills are always darker in colour. Even the microscopic characteristics are easy to differentiate: the Amethyst Deceiver has spherical and bristly spores while those of the Amethyst Agaric/Lilac Mycena are ellipsoid and smooth.

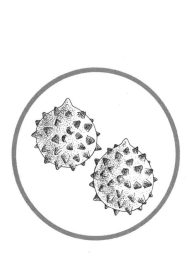

The spores of the Amethyst Deceiver

☠ Bitter Boletus

Tylopilus felleus (Bull. ex Fr.) P. Karst.

The cap is 60 to 120 mm wide, grey or greyish-brown, convex at first and later becoming arched to cushion-like. The surface of the cap is fibrillose when young, later becoming naked and matt. The tubes are white when young, later pink, 15 to 20 mm high, soon begin to swell or froth up, and they turn a rusty-brown with age or when pressed. The mouth of the tubes is tiny with circular angles. The stem is a dirty-white or brownish colour, slightly thicker at the bottom, 30 to 110 mm high and 10 to 25 mm wide, decorated with a distinctive dark brown network. The flesh is white, only a pale brownish colour beneath the skin of the cap, and hard in young fruit bodies but growing soft with age inside the cap, and fibrous in the stem. It has a very bitter taste and an inconspicuous but pleasant mushroom smell. The Bitter Boletus grows profusely in the summer and autumn in pine, spruce and mixed woods. It is inedible because of its strong bitter taste but does not cause any serious damage to health.

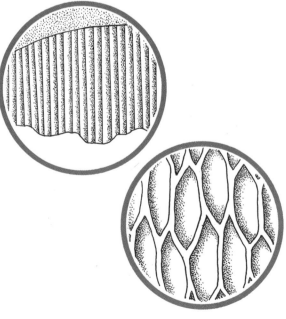

The tubes and network on the stem of the Bitter Boletus

Penny Bun Bolete

Boletus edulis Bull. ex Fr.

The cap is 50 to 200 mm in diameter, convex when young, later becoming arched, then broadly flattened out with age. It is cushion-like, sometimes depressed, fleshy, white at first then whitish, becoming dark brown with age and smooth. The tubes are 8 to 30 mm long, white at first, later light-yellow and turning yellow-green with age. The stem is club-shaped, swollen or cylindrical at the bottom, white, turning brown, with a white network at the top part. The flesh is white or whitish, with a delicate shade of cream beneath the skin of the cap, and a mildly sweet, pleasant mushroom taste and smell. It grows in the summer and autumn, mostly in mountain and highland spruce woods. In rare cases it can also be found under oaks and beeches in lowland areas. The amount of fruit bodies found is affected by the intensity of the picking and if all the young fruit bodies are picked one year then none will be found in following years. It is an excellent edible mushroom. It can be easily distinguished from the Bitter Bolete by its pleasant taste, distinctive white network on the stem and yellow-green tubes.

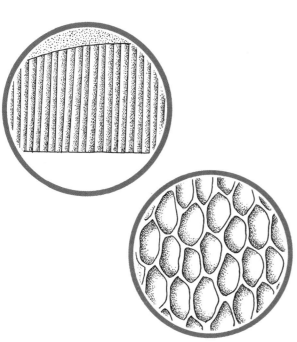

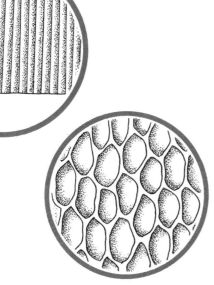

The tubes and network on the stem of the Penny Bun Bolete

☠ Disjointed Tricholoma

Tricholomataceae

Tricholoma sejunctum (Sow. ex Fr.) Quél.

The cap is 50 to 100 mm wide, arched to bell-shaped at first with an inrolled margin, later broadly flat, moderately hunched with a sharp straight or curved margin. The skin is dry, shiny, yellow-green to yellow-brown in colour, brownish in the middle, with fine dark-brown scales or pitted with radial strips, viscid when moist and easy to peel when older. The gills are narrowly attached to the stem, moderately thick, white, later getting a pleasant yellowish tint, then a mellow-brown colour when older; curved and torn at the edges. The stem is cylindrical, narrowing off and crooked at the base, 40 to 90 mm long and 10 to 30 mm wide, full, white or whitish with a delicate shade of yellow, turning slightly brown with age, smooth, naked or finely fibrous with a delicate shine. The flesh is white, but a pale yellow beneath the skin of the cap, with a cucumber, slightly bitter to sour taste, and a floury smell. It grows from August to October mostly in deciduous, rarely in coniferous, woodlands, and is not found at all in some regions. It is light to moderately poisonous, affecting the digestive tract (particularly fruit bodies picked in pine woods).

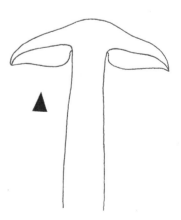

A cross-section of the Disjointed Tricholoma

Firwood Agaric; Man On Horseback

Tricholoma flavovirens (Pers. ex Fr.) Lund.

Dingy Agaric; Streaked Tricholoma

Tricholoma portentosum (Fr.) Quél.

Firwood Agaric; Man On Horseback
A detailed description is found on page 113. The Firwood Agaric/Man On Horseback grows from September to the beginning of November, mostly in pine woods with sandy ground. It is an excellent edible mushroom and versatile for cooking purposes. It can be distinguished from the Disjointed Tricholoma by its sulphur-yellow gills and delicious, sweet nutty taste.

Dingy Agaric; Streaked Tricholoma
A detailed description is found on page 109. The Dingy Agaric/Streaked Tricholoma grows from September to November in sandy pine woods. It differs from the Disjointed Tricholoma mainly in its delicious, nutty sweet taste, place of growth and the absence of shades of yellow-green on its cap.

Firwood Agaric; Man On Horseback

Dingy Agaric; Streaked Tricholoma

A cross-section of the Firwood Agaric/Man On Horseback

A cross-section of the Dingy Agaric/Streaked Tricholoma

☠ Tiger Tricholoma

Tricholoma pardinum Quél.

The cap is 50 to 120 mm in diameter, bell-shaped and arched when young, irregular, with an in-rolled margin, a knob in the middle; it is flatly bell-shaped with age with a thin to flat, dark to dirty grey-brown or brown-ash-coloured margin covered with fine fibrous scales that are usually broad but not too prominent. There are dense scales in the middle and so the middle of the cap is darker. The margin of the cap is pale with fine fibrous or almost tomentose scales. The gills are white or whitish later turning pale yellow but never going grey. They are broad, moderately dense, and sinuate at the stem. The stem is robust, full, a bit thicker at the base, white at the top, slightly ochre towards the bottom, sometimes turning dirty-ochre with age, pitted with fine fibres. The flesh is white, tough, does not change colour when cut and has a pleasant floury smell and taste. It is rare and grows in the summer and early autumn in coniferous and deciduous woodlands mainly on limestone ground. The fruit bodies appear individually and, in exceptional cases, are found in bigger clumps. It is highly poisonous, causing symptoms as early as one to two hours after consumption.

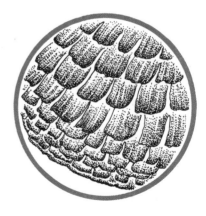

The surface of the cap of the Tiger Tricholoma

Grey Agaric; Mouse Tricholoma

Tricholoma terreum (Schaeff. ex Fr.) Kumm.

The cap is 40 to 80 mm wide, conically bell-shaped when young, soon becoming broadly flat with a small knob and a somewhat curved margin, dark grey or light ash to grey-brown in colour, tomentose at first, later with fibrous scales. The gills are moderately dense, quite high and decurrent, white, greyish when older, slightly serrated or wavy at the edges. The stem is cylindrical, full, cotton wool-like when older, later greyish pitted with fibres, fragile, soft and white-grained under the cap. The flesh in the cap is greyish, white in the stem, soft and fragile, indistinctive, but with a pleasant taste and a slight floury smell. It grows in clumps from September to November in deciduous and mixed woods, mostly in woodland glades and borders as well as in dense spruce and pine woods. It is most common in woods growing from poorer, sandy soils. It is an edible but not highly desirable mushroom, but is easy to find because of its abundance. It is easy to distinguish from the Tiger Tricholoma by the surface of its cap and smaller, more fragile fruit bodies. The Tiger Tricholoma has bigger scales on the surface of the cap and a more robust, thick stem; moreover it is very rare.

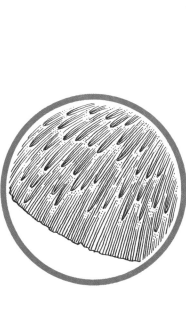

The surface of the cap of the Grey Agaric/ Mouse Tricholoma

☠ Roll Rim

Paxillus involutus (Batsch ex Fr.) Fr.

The cap is 40 to 110 mm wide, arched when young, later broadly flat, conspicuously inrolled, ochre-brown, brown-rusty or olive-brown in colour, turning brown in places where pressed; it is smooth on the surface, tomentose when young, later naked, dry, matt, very viscid in the rain. The gills are 4 to 6 mm high, thin, dense, decurrent at the stem, ochre when young, rusty-brown with age, going dark when pressed. The stem is cylindrical, full, 30 to 50 mm high, 10 to 20 mm wide, smooth, naked and brown-ochre in colour. The flesh is light-ochre in youth, later brownish, soft, juicy, of a sourish taste and pleasant smell. It grows from June to November in all types of forest. The fruit bodies grow mostly under birches in avenues, parks, orchards, groves; even in towns, e.g. a large number can be found growing in flower beds among several birches. Although its poisonous substances have not been examined, it is considered to be a dangerous mushroom.

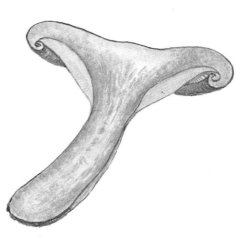

A cross-section of the fruit body of the Roll Rim

Glutinous Gomphidius

Gomphidius glutinosus (Schaeff. ex Fr.) Fr.

The cap is 50 to 110 mm in diameter, arched when young, slightly convex, later flat, depressed, even hollowed out; grey-brown, fleshy or chocolate brown, with black-brown spots appearing with age, smooth, covered with a thick layer of mucus which can be easily peeled off together with the skin. The gills are whitish when young, sparse, turning black with age, thick, low and decurrent. In youth they are cov-ered with a transparent mucous veil which forms an elevated mucous muscle with age. The stem is cylindrical, full, viscid, whitish at the top and lemon-yellow at the bottom. The flesh is soft, white, later turning light greyish, lemon-yellow at the base of the stem, indistinc-tive, slightly sour in taste and smell. It grows from July to October in coniferous woodlands on hills and far up in the mountains. It is found in great abundance in spruce woods. It is a tasty and edible mushroom, and is often pickled. It has a number of characteristics distinguishing it from the Roll Rim but even so it is still sometimes mistaken for the latter, as both are viscid and sticky on the surface. However the Glutinous Gomphidius has a thick layer of mu-cus and a cross-section of its fruit body shows the clear lemon-yellow colour of the flesh at the base of the stem.

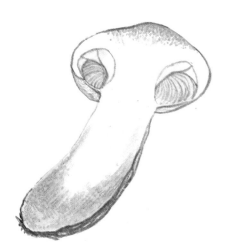

A cross-section of the Glutinous Gomphidius

☠ Leaden Entoloma

Entoloma lividum (Bull. ex St. Am.) Quél.

The cap is 50 to 150 mm in diameter, convex when young, later becoming arched with an in-rolled margin, then broadly flat with a rounded knob in the middle, sometimes also wavy; whitish, yellowish, greyish to ochre, with a silken shine, smooth, dry, fleshy and with a fibrous network. The gills are white-yellow when young and so dense that the very young fruit bodies cannot be distinguished. Mushroom pickers often think they are tubes and mistake the Leaden Entoloma for a bolete. When older, the gills are even free; when ripe the spores turn pink and end up a fleshy red colour. The stem is robust, cylindrical, thickly club-shaped at the bottom, white, later yellowish, full at first, then cotton wool-like or hollow, fibrous, flaky at the top. The flesh is firm, white, with a pleasant floury taste and smelling of fresh cucumbers. It grows from May to September in deciduous woodlands mostly on limy soils under oaks. It seeks out warmer sites. In its appearance it entices pickers but is poisonous causing serious stomach problems or even death. Do not confuse it with the St. George's Mushroom in woods. It can also be easily confused with the Clouded Clitocybe, the Buckler Agaric, the Dingy Agaric/Streaked Tricholoma or even – when young – with Oak Bolete. It can be distinguished from boletes by its gills and angular spores.

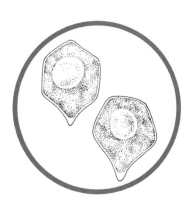

A young Leaden Entoloma and its spores

Clouded Clitocybe
Clitocybe nebularis (Fr.) Harmaja

Dingy Agaric; Streaked Tricholoma
Tricholoma portentosum (Fr.) Quél.

Clouded Clitocybe

Dingy Agaric; Streaked Tricholoma

Clouded Clitocybe

The cap grows 50 to 150 mm in height, is almost convex when young, later arched with an inrolled margin, with age becoming depressed with a sharp margin, with ash grey to grey white hoar. The gills are white, dense, and slightly decurrent at the stem. The stem is cylindrical, fibrous, white and greying. The flesh is white, with a sweetish smell and sweet mushroom taste (turning slightly sour with age). It grows abundantly from August to November in all kinds of woodland. It is edible but only the young fruit bodies are recommended for picking because of its strong aroma. It differs from the Leaden Entoloma in its whitish decurrent gills.

Dingy Agaric; Streaked Tricholoma

The cap measures 50 to 100 mm in diameter, is bell-shaped at first with an inrolled margin, later becoming arched, irregularly folded, grey to grey-black, streaked, smooth and shiny. The gills are sparse, decurrent at the stem, white with a tint of lemon-yellow. The flesh is white, with a nutty sweet taste and cucumber smell. It grows from September to November in sandy pine woods. It is an excellent edible mushroom. It never has pinkish gills in old age.

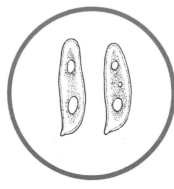

A young Oak Bolete and its spores

☠ Scrobiculate Milk Cap

Lactarius scrobiculatus (Scop. ex Fr.) Fr.

The cap measures 50 to 150 mm in diameter, is straw-yellow or yellow-ochre in colour, tough, fleshy, depressed in the middle, viscid, pitted with spots, has an inrolled margin that is flattened tomentose with raised hairs and a bald centre. The gills are 8 to 12 mm wide, attached to the stem, yellowish, pale, often with yellow edges, quite thin and dense. The stem is short, cylindrical, 40 to 60 mm long, 20 to 30 mm wide, pale, pale-yellow, full when young, later becoming hollow, pitted with ochre-rust spots (scrobiculate). The flesh is white, quite tough, and turns yellow from its milk. The milk is white and turns sulphur-yellow in the air. It has a sharp burning taste and flows profusely when the flesh is cut. It grows in the summer and autumn in dense highland coniferous woods, abundantly in places, elsewhere it is very rare; it is more abundant in acid soils. It has a strong burning taste and so is unsuitable for cooking. Some experts list it as a moderately poisonous species because the strong burning milk irritates the digestive tract and may cause vomiting and diarrhoea. Symptoms appear one to three hours after consumption.

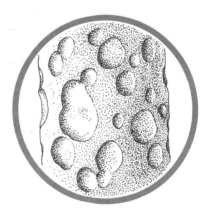

The stem of the Scrobiculate Milk Cap

Saffron Milk Cap;
Milky Agaric; Delicious Milk Cap

Lactarius deliciosus (L. ex Fr.) S.F. Gray

The cap is 30 to 150 mm wide, arched when young with an inrolled margin, later flat, depressed in the middle, almost funnel-shaped when older with a sharply folded margin, fleshy or orange-red with distinctive darker concentrated rings; at first fibrillose on the surface, later naked and viscid in the rain. The gills are 4 to 9 mm high, light fleshy red-yellow, turning green if injured, dense, fragile, decurrent at the stem. The stem is cylindrical, smooth, 30 to 60 mm high, 10 to 20 mm wide, red-orange, sometimes covered in orange spots when older, hollow and fragile. The flesh is whitish and when cut it releases a carrot red-coloured milk which turns green with oxidation. It has a very sharp, unpleasant taste, but an intensive and pleasant smell. It grows from August to November under pine trees. In recent years it has become more widespread and in certain regions it predominates over the Spruce Milk Cap. Its specific taste makes it best suited for pickling in vinegar or being smoked. It is easy to distinguish from the Scrobiculate Milk Cap by its unspotted (non-scrobiculate) stem and the carrot-coloured milk it releases.

The stem of the Saffron Milk Cap/Milky Agaric/Delicious Milk Cap

☠ # Plush Cortinarius

Cortinariaceae

Cortinarius orellanus (Fr.) Fr.

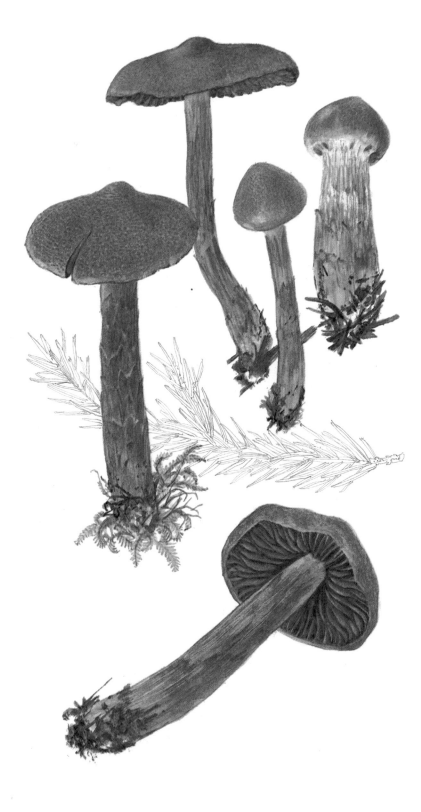

The cap is 35 to 100 mm in diameter, convex at first with an inrolled margin, later conically bell-shaped to broadly arched with a low rounded knob, irregularly curved and sometimes folded at the margin. The skin is not hygrophanous (does not change colour with a difference in moisture), and is velvet, tomentose, finely scaled, orange to red-brown and growing bald with age. The gills are sinuate and decurrent at the stem, sparse, thick, high to paunchy, a saffron-yellow at first, later turning orange-brown and a cinnamon-brown colour with age. When young they are covered with webbed fibres. The stem is cylindrical and often slightly pointed at the base, sometimes a bit curved, full, with lengthwise fibres, yellowish, going slightly brown with old age. The flesh in the cap is thin, only fleshy at the apex, firm, yellow-brown, with a mellow radish-like smell and taste; it is quite firm in the stem and the same colour as in the cap. It grows from August to October individually or in small clumps mostly in deciduous woods, especially under oaks in acid soils. In certain regions it is common, elsewhere it is a rarity or does not occur at all. It is a very dangerous, deadly poisonous mushroom.

A cross-section of the Plush Cortinarius

Firwood Agaric; Man On Horseback

Tricholoma flavovirens (Pers. ex Fr.) Lund.

The cap is 30 to 90 mm wide, arched with an inrolled margin when young, later broadly flat, with folds and a sharp margin, green-brown, olive or saffron-green-yellow in colour, usually darker, smooth, a little viscid when moist, often soiled. The skin can be peeled and may be a yellow-brown colour on fruit bodies growing in the open sun. The gills are moderately dense, decurrent at the stem, a bright sulphur-yellow. The stem is cylindrical, full, short, up to 20 mm wide, yellow, green-yellow or brown-yellow, usually dirty due to a thicker layer of soil at the base. The flesh is hard, fragile, white, a pale-yellow or lemon-yellow colour beneath the skin of the cap, with a pleasant floury smell and a delicious, sweetish nutty taste. It grows mainly in pine woods with sandy ground from September to the beginning of November, often in whole clumps or in so-called witches' rings. It is less commonly found under aspens or oaks. The Firwood Agaric/Man On Horseback is a versatile mushroom for cooking in view of its delicious taste. It differs from the Plush Cortinarius mainly in its lighter flesh colour, smell, taste and in the fact that when young its gills are not covered with web fibres.

The Firwood Agaric/Man On Horseback differs from the Plush Cortinarius mainly in the lighter colour of its flesh and bright yellow gills.

Deadly Cortinarius

Cortinarius speciosissimus Kühn. et Romagn.

The cap measures 25 to 80 mm in diameter, is convex at first with a slightly inrolled margin, later conically bell-shaped to arched and flat with a thick knob, light orange to orange-brown, with flaky scales sometimes folded at the margin. The skin is not hygrophanous (does not change colour when moist). The gills are deeply ingrowing into the stem, thick, up to 14 mm high and saffron-cinnamon in colour. When young they are covered with webbed fibres. The stem is cylindrical, thicker at the base and pointed, erect, full, with lengthwise fibres, 50 to 110 mm high, 5 to 15 mm wide, orange-brown with darker fibres. The flesh in the cap is thin but more fleshy at the apex, firm, a light saffron colour, with a radish-like smell and taste. In the stem it is quite firm and a similar colour to that in the cap. It grows from August to October sporadically, or in smaller clumps in pine and spruce woods, in boggy and peaty soil. It is highly poisonous. Like the Plush Cortinarius it contains substances which damage the liver and kidneys.

A cross-section of the Deadly Cortinarius shows the darker-coloured flesh.

Gypsy Mushroom

Rozites caperata (Pers. ex Fr.) P. Karst.

The cap is 40 to 100 mm wide, convex or cylindrical at first with an inrolled margin that becomes arched later, with age becoming broadly flat with a sharp margin and often with a blunt knob in the middle. When young it is whitish to violet-coloured and hoary, then goes bald, a clay-yellow colour, wrinkled when dry and cracked along the margin. The margin of the cap is joined to the stem by a thick membranous veil. The gills are 7 to 10 mm high, moderately dense, decurrent at the stem, yellow-ochre at first and covered with a membranous veil, later clay-ochre; with age it becomes rusty-brown, serrated and whitish at the edges. The stem is cylindrical to club-shaped at first, later cylindrical with a thicker base, full, 50 to 120 mm high, 10 to 20 mm wide, whitish, later ochre-coloured, with a silky shine, finely fibrous, smooth, naked and finely scaled above the ring. The ring has a double margin, is whitish when young, later yellowish. The flesh is whitish to yellowish, an ochre-yellow colour beneath the skin of the cap, unchanging when cut, with a pleasant taste and smell. It grows from August to October mainly in coniferous woods in lowlands and mountains. It is most common in acid soils. It is an edible mushroom and very tasty when cooked well. The young fruit bodies differ from the Deadly Cortinarius by the fact that they have gills covered with a membranous veil.

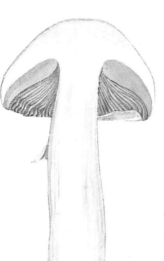

The Gypsy Mushroom has lighter flesh and a membranous ring.

☠ Purple-Red Cortinarius

Cortinarius phoeniceus (Bull.) ex R. Maire

The cap is 20 to 60 mm wide, acorn-shaped when young, later bluntly arched, flat with age with a blunt knob. The margin of the cap is slightly inrolled, later folded and lobed, the surface is dry, fibrous and silky, sometimes finely scaled and partly hygrophanous (going dark when moist). The skin is finely scaled, red-brown or chestnut-brown with a red tint. The gills are moderately dense, fragile, sinuated at the stem, covered with a webbed veil when young, blood red, with an olive tint when older. The stem is cylindrical, constantly yellow at the top under the cap, the other parts are ochre or orange-rust in colour with blood-red fibres. The web left over from the veil, is purple and, shaped like a ring, it remains on the upper third of the stem for a long time. It grows from July to the end of October in small clumps in acid soils under spruces, pines, less commonly under beeches. It is very widespread in places, and elsewhere not found at all. It is a poisonous mushroom and may cause serious harm to the liver and kidneys just as the Plush Cortinarius does (see page 112).

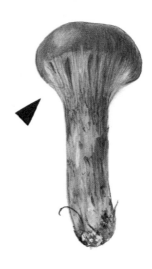

A webbed veil covers the gills of young cortinarius mushrooms.

Lacquered Laccaria

Laccaria proxima (Boud.) Pat.

The cap grows to a width of 35 to 70 mm, is convex at first, becoming flat with a marked knob, fibrillose, finely scaled when older, slightly grooved at the margin, a fleshy red or brown-orange colour, light ochre when dry. The gills are 3 to 10 mm high, sparse, adnate at the stem, dark pink, and covered in white spore dust when older. The stem is 40 to 100 mm long, 4 to 8 mm wide, cylindrical, with hollow tubes; the surface is covered with lengthwise fibres, red-brown or brown and slightly broader at the base, sometimes a twisted fusiform shape. The flesh is light red, tough, with a mellow mushroom taste and an indistinctive smell. It grows from July to November in coniferous and deciduous woodlands, usually under pines on sandy soil from lowlands to mountains. It also grows sporadically among peat-moss on boggy sites, on mountain pastures between woodland and under birches. It is an edible mushroom. Only pick the caps for cooking – the stem is too tough and fibrous. The younger fruit bodies of the Lacquered Laccaria can easily be distinguished from the Purple-Red Cortinarius because their gills are not so distinctively red and are not covered with a webbed veil.

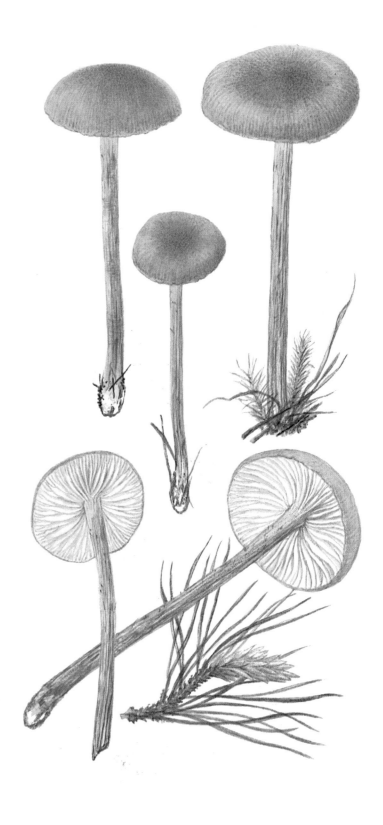

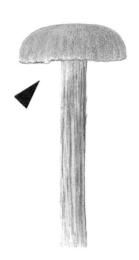

Laccaria mushrooms never have a veil.

☠ Lilac Conifer Cortinarius

Cortinarius traganus (Fr. ex Fr.) Fr.

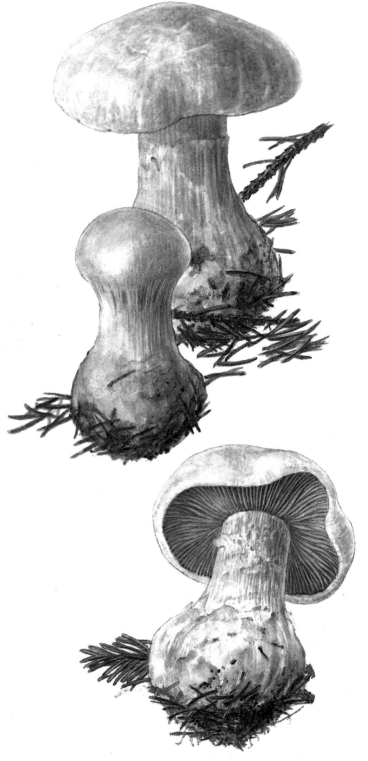

The cap is 40 to 160 mm wide, convex when young, light violet, with a silky shine, a violet web joined to the stem; when older it is arched to flat, light-ochre to whitish colour which fades, often cracked and dry. The margin is covered with remains of the veil which covered the young gills. The gills are moderately dense, attached to the stem, a saffron-ochre colour when young, rusty to rusty-brown with age. The stem is paunchy at first, later becoming club-shaped, full, lilac, fading to ochre, whitish at the base. The flesh is a dirty-yellow to yellow-brown, a bit rusty at the base of the stem, with a strong bitter taste and unpleasant smell when young resembling the smell of a goat shed. It grows abundantly from August to October in deciduous and coniferous woodlands, mostly in acid soils. It is regarded as moderately poisonous.

The Lilac Conifer Cortinarius has dark, unpleasant-smelling flesh

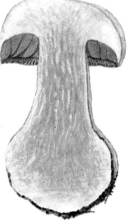

Gypsy Mushroom
Rozites caperata (Pers. ex Fr.) P. Karst.

Remarkable Cortinarius
Cortinarius praestans (Cord.) Gill.

Gypsy Mushroom

a detailed description of the Gypsy Mushroom is found on page 115. This tasty and popular mushroom can best be distinguished from the Lilac Conifer Cortinarius by its whitish to yellowish flesh and pleasant smell.

Remarkable Cortinarius

The cap measures 100 to 200 mm in diameter, is small when young, almost spherical, seated on a relatively large bulb to which it is connected by a veil. The margin of the cap is inrolled; when older the cap is arched; chestnut brown with a violet-copper tint, with finely ingrowing fibres, shiny, with flattened flaky remains of the veil and with conspicuous radial wrinkles on the margin. The gills are dense, whitish with an amethyst tint, later creamy, even rusty with age. They are sinuate at the stem and the edges are normally curved and serrated. The stem is full, club-shaped with a thick hoof-shaped base, covered with silky fibres, whitish-violet when young, becoming yellowish with a violet or whitish-coloured silky veil which tears into several scaly strips. The flesh is hard, whitish at first, later fair-coloured, with a mellow taste and indistinctive smell. It grows from August to the end of September mostly in deciduous hilly woodland on limestone ground. It is more common in western Europe. It is one of the good edible mushrooms and one of the bigger cortinarius mushrooms. It can be distinguished from the Lilac Conifer Cortinarius by its lighter flesh which does not smell unpleasant.

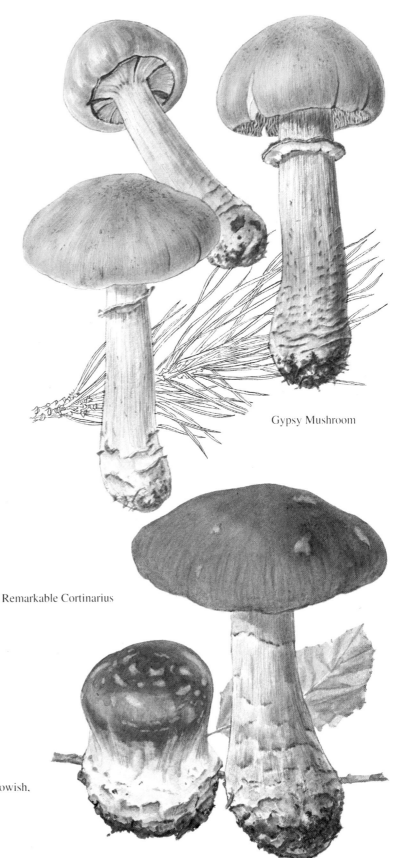

Gypsy Mushroom

Remarkable Cortinarius

The Gypsy Mushroom has yellowish, pleasant-smelling flesh.

☠ **Blood-Red Cortinarius**

Dermocybe sanguinea (Wulf. ex Fr.) Wünsche

The cap measures 20 to 50 mm in diameter, is arched when young, later flat, often with a knob, is thin-fleshed, matt, covered with fine flaky scale, dark blood-red or brown-purple in colour, fading when dry. The gills are dense, a rich blood to garnet-red colour, rounded, sinuate at the stem which, when older, is covered with a cinnamon-red from the spores that fall out. In early youth the gills are covered with a purple fibrous veil which breaks leaving fibrous remains on the stem. The stem is cylindrical, about 5 mm wide, slightly folded, narrowing off at the base, full when young, later resembling cotton wool or even hollow, fibrous and dark purple. The flesh is a red-purple, fades when dry, with a radish taste and smell. It grows from August to October on foothills and mountainous coniferous forests from woodland humus and on moss-covered stumps. It is quite a rare mushroom. Most experts do not classify it as a poisonous species but as an inedible mushroom. Research into its toxins is incomplete. Smaller red-coloured cortinarius mushrooms can easily be mistaken for laccarias.

All cortinarius mushrooms can easily be distinguished from laccarias by their webbed veil covering the young gills.

Deceiver

Laccaria laccata (Scop. ex Fr.) Cooke

The cap is 20 to 50 mm wide, arched when young, later flat, with a depressed pit in the middle, naked on the surface at first, then velvety to slightly scaly, grooved at the margin, transparent, fleshy red, red-brown or skin-coloured, ochre-cream when dry, covered in white spore dust with age. The stem is red-brown, fibrous, 30 to 70 mm high, 3 to 5 mm wide, firm, cylindrical, sometimes crooked. The flesh is thin, and a flushed pink colour which later fades, the stem is tough, with an indistinctive taste and smell. It grows from June to October in coniferous and deciduous woods, on woodland paths, in woodland ditches, parks and gardens, often in great clumps. Several good species grow in and around the area of the Deceiver which look very much like each other and can be easily confused when being determined. However all are edible. Pick only the caps for cooking as the stem is too tough. Make sure that the gills of younger fruit bodies are not covered with the webbed veil. That would show it to be one of the cortinarius mushrooms.

Laccaria mushrooms never have a veil.

☠ Ochre-Red Cortinarius

Cortinarius bolaris (Pers. ex Fr.) Fr.

The cap is 30 to 60 mm wide, convex when young, later broadly arched with a rounded knob, whitish, then yellowish, finally reddish to yellowish-saffron, covered in red flattened scales and dry. The gills are moderately dense, arched to decurrent at the stem, often branched, watery-brownish at first, later cinnamon-coloured turning a crimson-red when cut; when young they are covered with a small reddish web. The stem is cylindrical, hollow with age, yellowish, finally reddish, fibrous at first, later finely scaled in strips, going purple – even black – when pressed. The flesh is white, slowly turning red, with an indistinctive smell and bitter taste. It grows sparsely from August to September in beech and oak woods, mostly on damp sites, appearing in small clumps on favourable sites. It is a poisonous mushroom. The Ochre-Red Cortinarius may cause kidney damage and the poisoning requires medical treatment.

The gills of the Ochre-Red Cortinarius are brownish, later cinnamon-coloured.

Plums and Custard

Tricholomopsis rutilans (Schaeff. ex Fr.) Sing.

The cap measures 40 to 70 mm in diameter, when young it is bell-shaped with an inrolled margin, later broadly flat with a sharp margin. At first it is covered with appressed small red scales, then later separated from the transparent yellowish skin, dry and matt. The gills are moderately dense, decurrent at the stem, the edges are blunt and golden-yellow. The stem is cylindrical, tough, a bit paunchy when young, golden-yellow with purple to red flakes. The flesh is firm, juicy, a rich yellow colour, with a mildly sour taste and a slightly musty earthy smell. It grows abundantly from July to October on stumps and hidden roots of coniferous trees, especially pines, in lowlands and mountains, often in small clusters. It is one of the good edible mushrooms (particularly the small fruit bodies) but when cooked, Plums and Custard goes dark and sometimes acquires an earthy taste, which needs to be disguised in culinary use. For example Plums and Custard can be pickled, added to mushroom food mixtures or to doughs. It is not suitable for soups or cooked on its own. Plums and Custard can easily be distinguished from cortinarius mushrooms because it grows on wood, the young fruit bodies have no web and the gills are always a yellowish colour.

The gills of Plums and Custard are a yellowish colour.

☠ **Stinker**

Tricholoma sulphureum (Bull. ex Fr.) Kumm.

The cap is 20 to 70 mm wide, bell-shaped when young, soon becoming broadly flat with a rounded knob and thin. The skin is smooth, bald, shiny, sulphur-yellow to olive in colour, going slightly brown towards the middle. The gills are sparse, thick, sinuate, decurrent at the stem and sulphur-yellow in colour. The stem is cylindrical, usually quite long, full, like cotton wool or hollow when old, sulphur-yellow in colour with fine rusty-coloured fibres. The flesh is a sulphur-yellow colour throughout the fruit body, with a disgusting smell resembling coal gas and a slight burning and unpleasant taste. It grows from July to November in deciduous, to a lesser extent also in coniferous woodlands, most often under beeches, where it appears in large clumps. It is here that it can be mistaken for the Firwood Agaric/Man On Horseback which grow under beeches but are a great rarity in deciduous woods. The Stinker is a poisonous mushroom causing digestive problems and vomiting one to three hours after consumption. It contains a large amount of indulin substances.

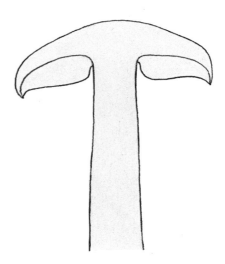

A cross-section of the fruit body of the Stinker (the flesh in its stem is of a distinctive yellow colour).

Firwood Agaric; Man On Horseback

Tricholoma flavovirens (Pers. ex Fr.) Lund.

A detailed description is found on page 113. When picking the Firwood Agaric/Man On Horseback in a mixed or deciduous wood, careless mushroom pickers sometimes mistake it for the Stinker. It often happens to smokers who have a dulled sense of smell and cannot distinguish the disgusting smell of the Stinker. Fortunately the poison is not fatal. Nevertheless it is good to recall the distinguishing character-istics of the Firwood Agaric/Man On Horse-back. This excellent mushroom, versatile for cook-ing, differs from the Stinker mostly in its pleasant floury smell, delicious taste, light flesh and dense gills.

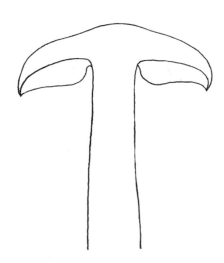

A cross-section of the Firwood Agaric/Man On Horseback

☠ Brown Parasol

Lepiota helveola Bres.

The cap measures 15 to 40 mm in diameter, is convex when young, later flat with a knob, flaky at the margin, the skin is like fine plush and dry; the younger fruit bodies have a rich red-brown skin that is lighter at the margins with a tint of pink. When old, irregular oblong scales appear on the surface of the cap arranged into almost compact rings, fleshy-red to brick-red in colour, that are minute and overlap the margin of the cap by about 1 mm. The dirty pink surface of the cap can be detected between the scales. The gills are dense, white, quite high and detached from the stem. The stem is fibrous, scaly, balding and the same colour as the cap. There is a disappearing scaly whitish ring. Above it is a stem covered in very fine white fibres. The flesh is white, and goes pink when dried out, without a distinctive taste and smell. It grows from August to October on grassy sites in the gardens, pastures and woodland borders of warmer regions. It is more abundant on limestone ground but is classed as one of the rarer species. It is one of the smaller reddish parasol (or lepiota) mushrooms which contain similar poisonous substances to the Death Cap. Therefore, they cause phalloidine poisoning with consistent diarrhoea, vomiting and subsequent liver damage. Treatment is the same as for Death Cap poisoning. It can be mistaken for the Large Grey Agaric/Shaggy Parasol or the Fairy-Ring Champignon.

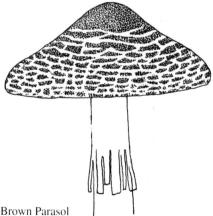

The cap of the Brown Parasol

Large Grey Agaric; Shaggy Parasol

Macrolepiota rhacodes (Vitt.) Sing.

A detailed description is given on pages 45 and 131. The Large Grey Agaric/Shaggy Parasol grows individually or in large clumps from June to October in deciduous and coniferous woodlands mostly on warmer and drier sites. Its mycelium remains on one site for several years. It is found in acacia woods which are relatively poor in the diversity of mushroom species. The light variety of this parasol mushroom can sometimes be found growing in gardens with manured soil and on compost hence it is known as the Garden Parasol (var. *hortensis*). The Large Grey Agaric/Shaggy Parasol is one of the excellent edible mushrooms but mushroom pickers pick it less often than the Parasol Mushroom, maybe because they are put off by the reddening flesh. It can be distinguished from the Brown Parasol by its bigger fruit body and the colour changes of its flesh when cut. The Large Grey Agaric/Shaggy Parasol turns a saffron-yellow colour at first and then red when injured whereas the flesh of the Brown Parasol is constantly white.

Large Grey Agaric; Shaggy Parasol

Fairy-Ring Champignon

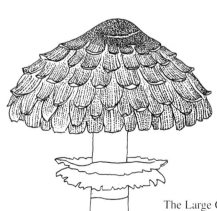

The Large Grey Agaric/Shaggy Parasol has distinctive scales on the surface of its cap.

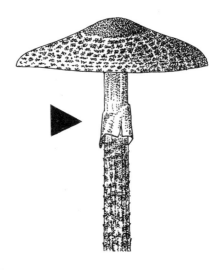

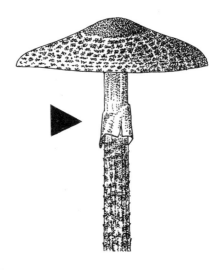

☠ Dark Parasol

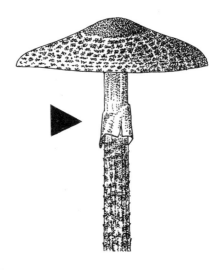

Lepiota fuscovinacea Moell. et J. Lange

Agaricaceae

The cap is 30 to 50 mm wide, convex when young, later broadly bell-shaped with a rounded knob, flat in old age but retaining the knob, a dark red-brown at first, fibrillose, cracking into rather fine raised scales or covered with fine clumps of hair. The gills are covered with a grey-violet web at first and are free, dense and white when old. The stem is erect, cylindrical, bald and white at the top, otherwise covered with densely wavy purple-lilac fibres, grey-brown in colour lower down, with a whitish, fibrous and membranous ring. The flesh is thin, white, silky and a pale wine colour between the scales, with an indistinctive taste and mellow fruity smell. It grows very sparsely on limestone ground in warm regions. It contains the poisonous substances of the Death Cap just like other small coloured parasol mushrooms. It causes phalloidine poisoning if consumed, accompanied by persistent diarrhoea and heavy vomiting and finally causes liver damage. Treatment is the same as for Death Cap poisoning. In rare cases the Dark Parasol is mistaken for the Deceiver or Fairy-Ring Champignon.

The Dark Parasol has a clearly evident ring on its stem.

Deceiver 🍴

Laccaria laccata (Scop. ex Fr.) Cooke

Tricholomataceae

Fairy-Ring Champignon 🍴

Marasmius oreades (Bolt. ex Fr.) Fr.

Deceiver

A detailed description of the Deceiver is found on page 121. Notice particularly the stem and gills when picking it. Unlike the Dark Parasol, the Deceiver has no ring on its stem and its gills are a light fleshy red colour. When old they are covered with dust and look as though they are lacquered.

Fairy-Ring Champignon

The cap measures 15 to 35 mm, is bluntly conical or convex when young, later becoming flat with a blunt knob in the centre. Its margin is finely grooved away from the translucent gills. It is smooth, tan or light flesh-coloured, going darker when moist. The gills are very sparse, high and sinuate at the stem and a little lighter than the cap. The stem is cylindrical, long, slender, full, hoary, light-ochre, white and tomentose at the base, flexible, very tough, unbreakable. The mushroom has whitish, thin flesh with a pleasant taste and bitter almond-like smell. The Fairy-Ring Champignon grows from May to October on grassy sites – boundaries, meadows, gardens – in lowlands and mountains. It is an excellent edible mushroom, particularly suitable for soups. The caps are not picked. The Fairy-Ring Champignon differs from the Dark Parasol by the absence of a ring on its very flexible stem. The surface of the cap is smooth like that of the Deceiver and is not scaly.

Deceiver

Fairy-Ring Champignon

The Deceiver (left) and the Fairy-Ring Champignon (right) have no ring.

☠ **Sharp Scaly Parasol**

Lepiota aspera (Pers. ex Fr.) Quél.

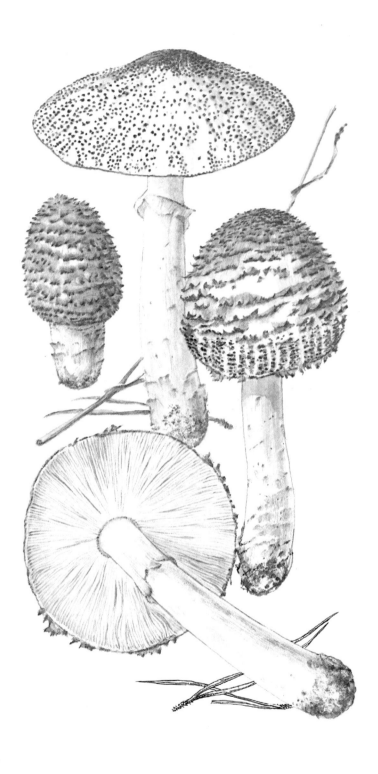

The cap is 50 to 110 mm wide, convex at first, later arched to flat, tomentose, a tobacco-brown colour, densely covered with bristly, erect, prickly black-brown scales; the scales break away easily in old age. The gills are white, dense, free and quite high. The stem is erect, easily breakable, cylindrical, thicker at the base with a low smooth bulb, with hollow tubes when old, whitish and smooth above the ring and with fine hairs underneath, whitish with numerous brown raised bristles which overlap the ring. When young the gills are covered with a fibrous veil which later forms a narrow red-brown scaly ring. The flesh is white, slightly sour in taste and with a distinctive smell resembling the Earth Ball or Variegated Bolete. It grows rarely from July to October in all kinds of woodland or gardens. It is a slightly poisonous mushroom, causing diarrhoea and vomiting. Small amounts of the Death Cap toxins have also been found in it.

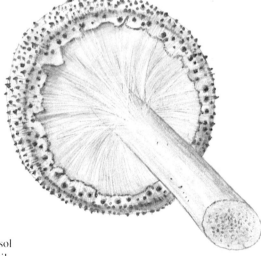

The young fruit body of the Sharp Scaly Parasol
– the gills are still covered with the fibrous veil.

Large Grey Agaric; Shaggy Parasol

Macrolepiota rhacodes (Vitt.) Sing.

The cap measures 90 to 140 mm in diameter, is almost spherical when young, later bell-shaped and arched; when older, broadly flat with a knob in the middle; the surface is cracked up into conspicuous large, at first light brown, later darker scales that are densely laid out like tiles and are raised; only in the middle of the cap around the knob does the skin remain unbroken. The gills are dense, high, free at the stem, rounded at the margin, white but turn red when injured. When young they are covered with a membranous veil. The stem is cylindrical, breakable and thickens out at the bottom into a bulb, with hollow tubes, whitish at first, brownish later, reddening in places where pressed, with a movable double white ring on the upper part. The flesh is white, turns a saffron yellow when cut at first, then goes red and finally brown. The cap turns cotton wool-like and the stem becomes woody. It has a pleasant sweet taste, sometimes a bit nutty and a distinctive mushroom smell. It grows quite abundantly from June to October in deciduous and coniferous woodlands, gardens, parks and purely acacia woods in lowland and highland areas. The fruit bodies appear sporadically and in great clumps. It is a very good edible mushroom. It differs from the Sharp Scaly Parasol in its membranous veil when young, and the different nature of the scales on the surface of its cap in the older fruit bodies. A good distinguishing sign is also the pleasant mushroom smell of the Large Grey Agaric/Shaggy Parasol as opposed to the distinctive Earth Ball-like stink of the Sharp Scaly Parasol.

The younger fruit body of the Large Grey Agaric/Shaggy Parasol

131

☠ Scaly-Stalked Hebeloma

Cortinariaceae

Hebeloma sinapizans (Paulet ex Fr.) Gill.

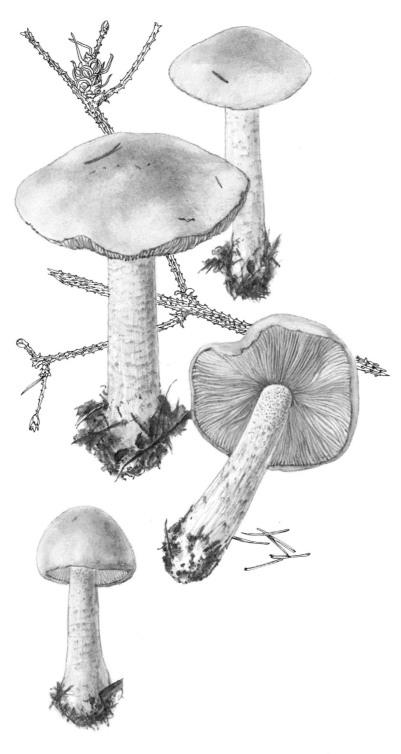

The cap is 80 to 120 mm wide, a brick red colour, later lighter, smooth, bald, only a little viscid, arched, flat when old, clay-brown to cinnamon, high and whitish when young. The stem is pale, cracking up into fibrous scales, cylindrical, broadening out at the bottom into a small bulb and with fibrous flesh. It grows sporadically from August to October in deciduous and mixed woodlands from lowland to highland areas, in parks it is found mainly growing under beeches. It is not rare and is moderately poisonous. No detailed research has been made into this mushroom as yet. It is sometimes mistaken for the Sandy/Poplar Tricholoma or for the late growing St. George's Mushroom. Poisoning by the Scaly-Stalked Hebeloma causes discomfort, vomiting and diarrhoea.

A cross-section of the fruit body of the Scaly-Stalked Hebeloma

Sandy/Poplar Tricholoma

Tricholoma populinum J. Lange

The cap measures 50 to 150 mm in diameter, is arched or convex with an inrolled margin when young, turning broadly flat when older with a straight margin, fleshy and tough. The skin is grey-brown to fleshy red-brown, darker at the apex and two-thirds of it can be peeled off, sometimes it is also spotted. The gills are sinuate and decurrent at the stem, dense, whitish to skin-coloured, turning a rusty colour when old. The stem is cylindrical, swollen at the bottom, root-like, full, smooth and with floury hoar at the top, white then turning finely rusty in colour. The flesh remains purely white, fleshy and brownish under the skin of the cap, and has a floury cucumber smell. It tastes like floury cucumber at first but soon becomes bitter. It grows from August to October under poplars in woodlands, groves, orchards and avenues in lowlands and highlands. The fruit bodies may grow next to a tree in a meadow that is some distance from a wood. They can grow abundantly in one locality for a number of years. It is a highly suitable mushroom for cooking and is particularly good for picking because it has firm flesh. It can be used for making sauces and soups. The bitter taste disappears when cooked. It can be easily distinguished from the Scaly-Stalked Hebeloma by the consistency of its flesh and the floury cucumber smell. However, it is more difficult to distinguish from the similar brown tricholomas which are mostly poisonous. Take particular notice of the kind of tree under which you pick the mushroom; the Sandy/Poplar Tricholoma always grows under a poplar, as its name signifies.

A cross-section of the Sandy/Poplar Tricholoma

☠ Poison Pie

Hebeloma crustuliniforme (Bull. ex St. Am.) Quél.

The cap measures 40 to 70 mm in diameter, is light grey-ochre in colour, sometimes dark brown though always lighter around the circumference, smooth, naked, viscid when moist and often folded. The gills are dense, whitish, later a clay-brown colour releasing drops of bitter watery juice which, when dried out, leaves behind dark spots. The stem is cylindrical, broader at the bottom, resembling cotton wool when young, later hollow, whitish to cream, covered in small grains at the top. The flesh is whitish to light cream, with a radish smell and unpleasant, sometimes sickening, bitter taste. It grows from May to October in woods, woodland meadows, avenues, parks and everywhere where there are sufficient remains of vegetation. It is a moderately poisonous mushroom. It can sometimes find its way into food if care is not taken when picking late growing St. George's Mushrooms or the Sandy/Poplar Tricholoma. If cooked or if herbs are added to a dish containing this mushroom then it can taste pleasant, but may cause discomfort, vomiting and stomach pains.

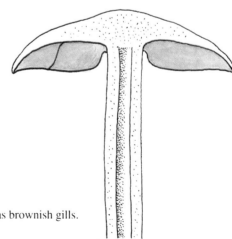

The Poison Pie has brownish gills.

134

St. George's Mushroom
Calocybe gambosa (Fr.) Donk

Sandy/Poplar Tricholoma
Tricholoma populinum J. Lange

St. George's Mushroom
A detailed description is found on page 31. St. George's Mushroom grows abundantly from April to June in all woodlands, mostly in grass in woodland borders, along paths, in gardens and parks, and above all under deciduous trees and bushes in lowland and highland areas. It can also occasionally be found on grassy sites, meadows and pastures. In rare instances it can be found on naked woodland soil, sometimes even in the autumn. It is a good edible mushroom suitable for all sorts of dishes. It can be distinguished from the Poison Pie mostly by its pleasant floury smell and delicious, floury cucumber taste. An important distinguishing characteristic are the constantly white gills which are so dense in youth that they resemble the closed leaves of a book.

Sandy/Poplar Tricholoma
A detailed description is found on page 134. It can be distinguished form the Poison Pie by its cucumber floury smell and more pleasant taste. Another distinguishing characteristic are the gills which have no dark stains as have those of the Poison Pie.

St. George's Mushroom

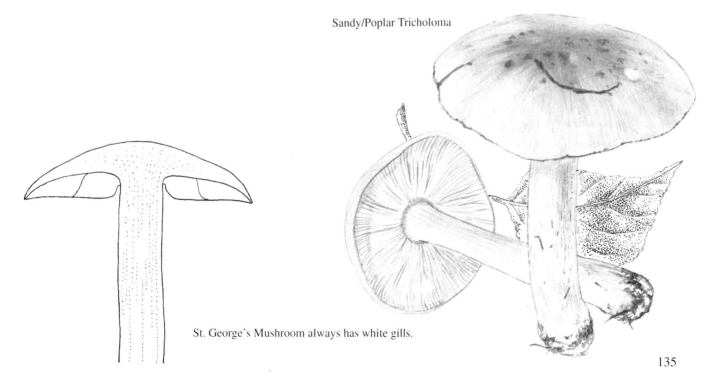

Sandy/Poplar Tricholoma

St. George's Mushroom always has white gills.

135

☠ Striped Tricholoma

Tricholoma virgatum (Fr. ex Fr.) Kumm.

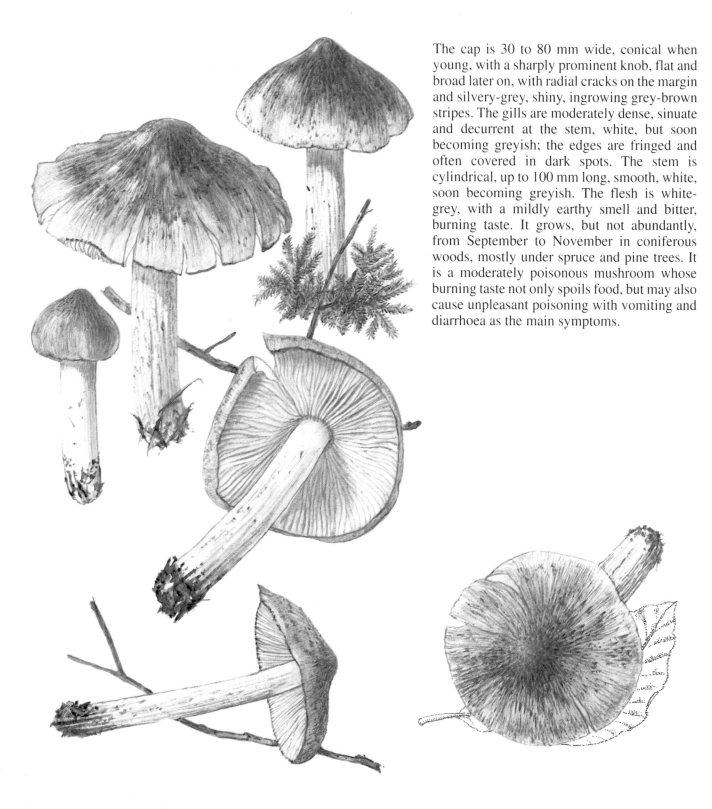

The cap is 30 to 80 mm wide, conical when young, with a sharply prominent knob, flat and broad later on, with radial cracks on the margin and silvery-grey, shiny, ingrowing grey-brown stripes. The gills are moderately dense, sinuate and decurrent at the stem, white, but soon becoming greyish; the edges are fringed and often covered in dark spots. The stem is cylindrical, up to 100 mm long, smooth, white, soon becoming greyish. The flesh is white-grey, with a mildly earthy smell and bitter, burning taste. It grows, but not abundantly, from September to November in coniferous woods, mostly under spruce and pine trees. It is a moderately poisonous mushroom whose burning taste not only spoils food, but may also cause unpleasant poisoning with vomiting and diarrhoea as the main symptoms.

The Striped Tricholoma has ingrowing fibres on the surface of its cap.

Grey Agaric; Mouse Tricholoma

Tricholoma terreum (Schaeff. ex Fr.) Kumm.

A detailed description of the mushroom is found on page 105. When picking the Grey Agaric/Mouse Tricholoma, which is commonly found growing in all kinds of woodland, it is unnecessarily mistaken for the Striped Tricholoma. The Grey Agaric/Mouse Tricholoma grows in clumps from September to November in coniferous and mixed woodlands mostly in woodland glades and on borders, and in parks as well as in dense spruce and pine woods. It is most often found in woodlands growing from poorer soils throughout the temperate zone of the Northern hemisphere and Africa. It is an edible mushroom, although of inferior quality but thanks to its mass occurrence, it can be easily found. It is added to various mushroom mixtures, soups, and is suitable for drying and pickling. It can be easily distinguished from the Striped Tricholoma by its indistinctive, but pleasant taste (the Striped Tricholoma has a bitter and even a burning taste when raw), and by the tomentose or fibrous scaly cap (the surface of the cap of the Striped Tricholoma is smooth, shiny, with ingrowing grey-brown fibres).

The Grey Agaric/Mouse Tricholoma has a tomentose or fibrous scaled cap.

☠ **Sheathed Agaric; Grisette**

Amanita vaginata (Bull. ex Fr.) Quél.

The cap is 30 to 90 mm wide, conical or bell-shaped when young, soon becoming broadly flat with a small knob, grey to grey-brown, with conspicuous grooves far from the margin; thin flesh, fragile, mostly naked or only with sporadic torn remains of the veil. The young fruit body of the Sheathed Agaric/Grisette resembles a small egg. When the veil bursts, a pointed volva forms at the bottom of the stem. The skin of the cap is sticky when young, bald when dry, and shiny. The gills are free, dense, high, fragile and white. The stem is breakable, erect, long, broadening out conically at the bottom, smooth or finely scaled, white or greyish, with-out a ring, covered with a high, free, pointed white volva at the bottom of the stem. The flesh is whitish, filled with water, very fragile, with a mildly sweet taste and indistinctive smell. It grows profusely from June to September in deciduous and coniferous woodlands in acid soils, particularly under birches. The raw mushroom is very poisonous – it must always be cooked thoroughly before being served. Take care not to confuse it with the unusual fruit body of the Death Cap from which it can be distinguished (as can all grisettes) by the fact that it has no ring.

Common Volvariella ¶¶

Volvariella speciosa (Fr.) Sing.

Brown-Yellow Amanita ¶¶

*Amanita umbrinolut*ea Secr.

Common Volvariella

The Common Volvariella is described in detail on page 51. Here is a recap of the typical char-acteristics by which it can be recognised. The cap is 60 to 120 mm wide, with a dirty-white, greyish to brownish skin. The gills are whitish when young, fleshy pink when old. The stem is white, without a ring, enveloped in a loose, pointed and lobed whitish volva. The flesh is white, with the taste and smell of honey and potatoes. The Common Volvariella differs from the Sheathed Agaric/Grisette especially in the fleshy pink colour of its gills when old, and in the place that it grows – on well manured sites outside woodlands, in fields, near compost, in gardens and parks.

Brown-Yellow Amanita

The cap is 50 to 120 mm wide, egg-shaped when young, and enclosed in a white case, broadly flat when old, a rusty-brown colour, distinctively grooved at the margin, viscid when moist, otherwise shiny and smooth. The gills are dense, high, white and free. The stem is cylindrical at the base, growing from a free, pointed greyish volva; it has no ring. The flesh is white, watery, very fragile, and has a pleasant sweet taste and indistinctive smell. It grows from July to October in highland and mountain spruce woods. It is an edible and tasty mushroom. It differs from the Sheathed Agaric/Grisette mainly in the rusty brown colour of its cap.

Common Volvariella

The edible Brown-Yellow Amanita can be distinguished mainly by the colour of its cap.

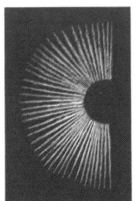 

Grisettes have a white spore dust, the Common Volvariella has pink spores (right).

☠ **Summer Tricholoma**

Tricholoma aestuans Fr.

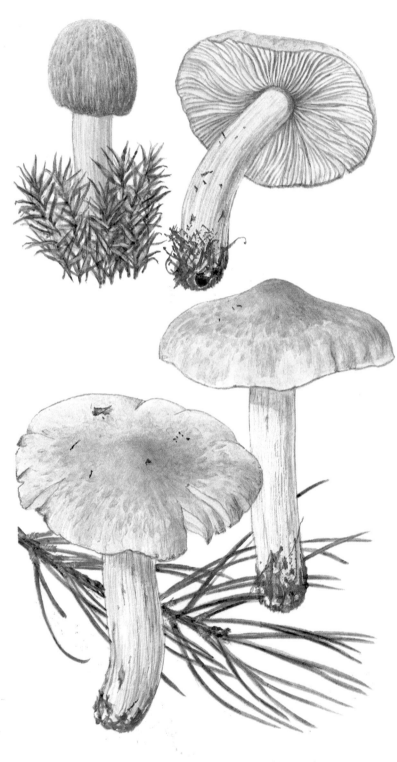

The cap measures 30 to 80 mm in diameter; when young it is conical with an inrolled margin, later it is broad, flat and slightly depressed with a tiny knob in the centre and slightly curved margin. The skin is light olive-yellow with lengthwise ingrowing fibres, smooth; when older, finely scaled around the knob, going slightly brown, viscid when moist. The gills are moderately dense, decurrent at the stem, a greenish rich-yellow colour when young, becoming pale yellow-olive, serrated and going brown. The stem is cylindrical, full, short (but longer if the mushroom grows from deep humus), flexible, fibrous to finely grooved, olive-coloured when young, fading later. The flesh is white, later yellowish, of an indistinctive to slightly floury smell and bitter at first, with a distinctive burning taste. It grows sporadically from September to November mostly in sandy pine woods together with the Firwood Agaric/Man On Horseback; it is not found in acid soil. It is a mildly poisonous mushroom causing digestive problems and vomiting.

A cross-section of the Summer Tricholoma – apart from the bitterish taste of its flesh it can also be distinguished from the Firwood Agaric/Man On Horseback by the yellowish flesh in older fruit bodies.

Firwood Agaric/Man On Horseback

Tricholoma flavovirens (Pers. ex Fr.) Lund.

A detailed description is found on page 113. The Firwood Agaric/Man On Horseback grows mostly in pine woods with sandy soil. The fruit bodies appear from September to the beginning of November, often in entire clumps or so-called witches' rings. It is a versatile mushroom for cooking, with a delicious, sweet nutty taste and firm consistency of the flesh. The Summer Tricholoma betrays itself by the bitter and distinctive burning taste of its flesh.

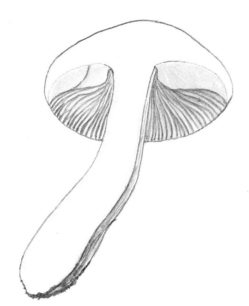

A cross-section of the Firwood Agaric/Man On Horseback

☠ Bitter/Sardonyx Russula

Russula chrysodacryon Sing.

The cap measures 50 to 100 mm in diameter, is convex when young, later becoming broadly arched, flat and slightly depressed, dark-violet, cloudy-purple, greyish or cloudy olive-green in colour, often with yellow specks. The skin is matt, sticky only when young. The gills are dense, low, viscid when moist, yellowish in youth, becoming butter yellow with age. The stem is cylindrical, hard, full, lemon-yellow with a purple-violet tinge as though hoary. The flesh is firm, lemon-yellow and turning saffron in colour at those spots where injured but purple beneath the skin of the cap, with a pleasant fruity smell but an instantly unbearable burning taste. It grows from July to October in coniferous woodlands. The mushroom contains a considerable amount of resinous substances which greatly irritate the digestive tract. A good test for this mushroom is to put some ammonia solution on the stem – it will go red.

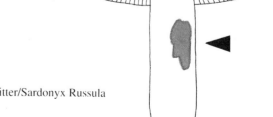

The chemical reaction of the Bitter/Sardonyx Russula to a solution of ammonia

Blue and Yellow Russula; Variegated Russula

Russula cyanoxantha (Schaeff. ex Schw.) Fr.

🍴

Russula Heterophylla

Russula heterophylla (Fr.) Fr.

🍴

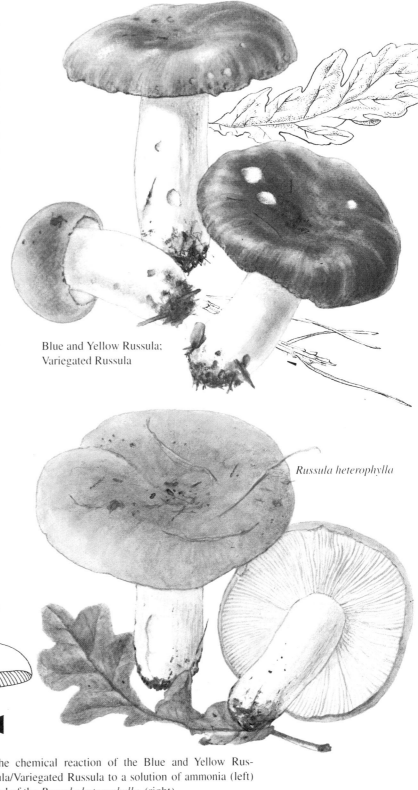

Blue and Yellow Russula;
Variegated Russula

Russula heterophylla

Blue and Yellow Russula; Variegated Russula

The cap is 60 to 150 mm wide, almost spherical when young, later convex to arched, broadly flat when older and slightly depressed in the middle; viscid when moist, a washed-out violet to purple-bluish or greenish colour and often fading in the centre. The skin can be peeled only up to a third of the cap. The gills are 5 to 10 mm high, thin, moderately dense, pure white, flexible, and unbreakable. The stem is cylindrical, white, in rare cases slightly bluish in colour and naked. The flesh is hard, firm, flexible, juicy, white, has a dull taste and indistinctive smell. It grows from June to October in deciduous and coniferous woodlands. It is one of the tastiest of the Russula mushrooms. It can be reliably distinguished from the Bitter/Sardonyx Russula by the flexible gills and the negative reaction of the flesh on a solution of ammonia (the Bitter/Sardonyx Russula immediately turns red when coming into contact with ammonia).

Russula heterophylla

The cap measures 60 to 120 mm in diameter, is convex when young, later becoming arched to flat, slightly depressed in the middle; yellow-green, olive-green, sometimes black-brown in the centre, then fading. The gills are dense, arched, white, yellowing or going rusty with age. The stem is short, cylindrical, narrowing off at the base, white and going rust. The flesh is white, with a delicious taste and indistinctive smell. It grows from July to October in deciduous woodlands. It is an excellent edible mushroom. The mushroom is easily distinguishable from the green russulas in its delicious taste. It has a negative reaction to a solution of ammonia.

The chemical reaction of the Blue and Yellow Russula/Variegated Russula to a solution of ammonia (left) and of the *Russula heterophylla* (right)

☠ Reddish Brown Russula; Bay Russula

Russulaceae

Russula badia Quél.

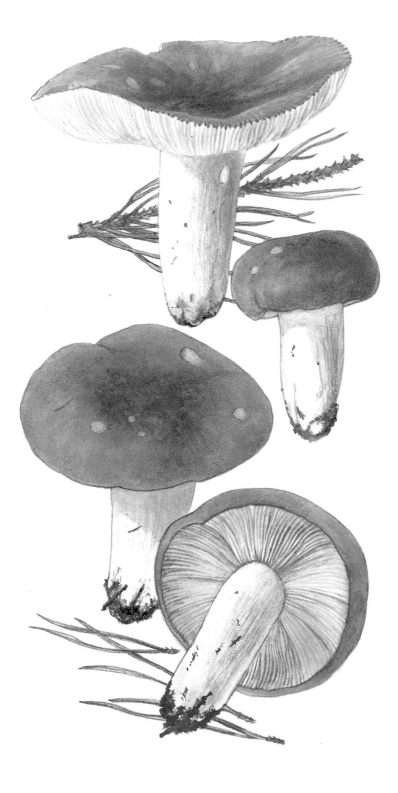

The cap measures 50 to 120 mm in diameter, is convex when young, soon becoming flat, with a broad to shallow depression; blood red, red-brown or violet brown, either nearly black or yellowish in the centre; and a third of the skin can be peeled. The gills are dense, paunchy, narrow, white at first, later light yellow, the edges are pinkish sometimes. The stem is cylindrical or club-shaped, white with a tint of pink. The flesh is white, turning rusty with age or if pressed; the smell resembles cedar wood, and the taste is dull at first, but leaves a sharp taste in the mouth for up to half an hour. It grows from July to November in coniferous woodlands mostly under pines. It is inedible and moderately poisonous.

The negative reaction of the Reddish Brown Russula/ Bay Russula to a green vitriol solution

Shrimp Russula
Russula xerampelina (Schaeff. ex Secr.) Fr. 🍴

Edible Russula
Russula vesca Fr. 🍴

Shrimp Russula

The cap is 40 to 120 mm wide, convex when young, later becoming arched, flat and depressed; highly variable in colour (wine red, crimson, pink, olive to brown), matt, hoary in when young, and half of the skin can be peeled. The gills are dense, whitish at first, later creamy ochre, turning brown when pressed. The stem is cylindrical, whitish, often reddish in places, turning brown when pressed. The flesh is creamy and turns brown if injured, has a mildly sweetish taste and a fish-like smell, particularly fruit bodies that are drying up. It grows abundantly from July to October in all woodlands. It is a very good edible mushroom. It can be distinguished from the Reddish Brown Russula/Bay Russula by its fish smell and the green reaction of the flesh to a green vitriol solution.

Edible Russula

The cap measures 50 to 80 mm in diameter, is almost spherical at first, later arched then broad and flat, slightly depressed in the centre; of a cloudy to fleshy red colour, often faded, sometimes yellowish to whitish in colour. The skin is naked, matt when dry. The gills are 7 to 9 mm high, dense, rounded at the edges, lowest at the stem and a little decurrent, white – often with rusty specks. The stem is cylindrical, narrow to pointed at the bottom, a ginger colour and very hard. The flesh is white, hard and turning rusty on disturbed spots, with a hazelnut-like taste and indistinctive smell. It grows abundantly in the summer and autumn, in light deciduous woods. It is a very tasty mushroom. It can be safely distinguished from the Reddish Brown Russula/Bay Russula by applying a drop of green vitriol solution. The flesh of the Edible Russula turns orange while there is a negative reaction in the Reddish Brown Russula/Bay Russula.

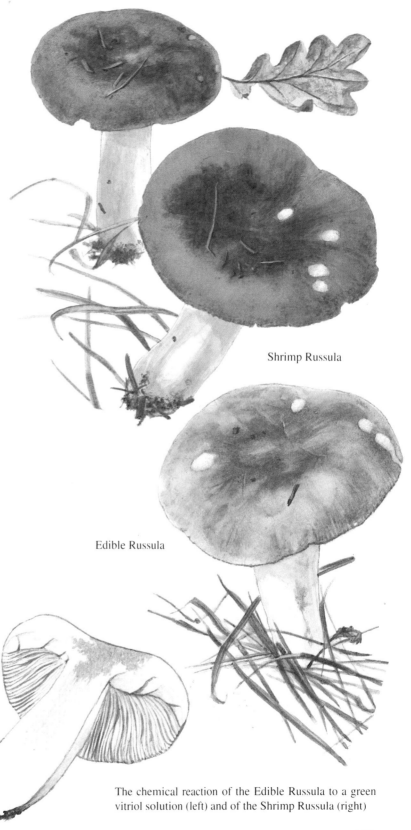

Shrimp Russula

Edible Russula

The chemical reaction of the Edible Russula to a green vitriol solution (left) and of the Shrimp Russula (right)

145

☠ Unicoloured Galerina

Galerina unicolor (Fr.) Sing.

The cap is 5 to 30 mm in size, convex at first, later becoming conical or bell-shaped with a prominent knob, light brown-ochre when dry, red to orange-brown when damp, grooved around the circumference. The gills are broad, paunchy, often triangular, adnate at the stem, pale-ochre in youth, later a fair cinnamon-brown. The stem is tubed, slender, almost bald, cinnamon-brown, darker at the bottom; the upper part has quite an enduring ring. The ring is thin, raised, often a raised funnel shape, pale ochre. The flesh in the cap is thin, light rusty-brown, with a mild floury taste and smell. It grows from August to October in small clusters on coniferous tree stumps and quite resembles the Marginate Galerina (see page 147), but is smaller with wider gills and less transparent cap at the margin. It is a close relative of the Marginate Galerina and probably contains similar poisonous substances, and may be dangerous.

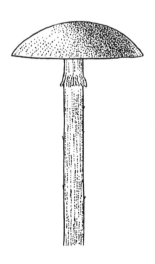

The Unicoloured Galerina has an almost bald stem.

Changeable Agaric; Changeable Pholiota

Kuehneromyces mutabilis (Schaeff. ex Fr.) Sing. et Smith

The Changeable Agaric or Changeable Pholiota (a detailed description is found on page 149), is a small mushroom which can be found by mushroom pickers from spring to autumn. It grows in rich clusters on stumps and dead roots of deciduous trees, usually birches or lindens. Like the Spruce Milk Cap it is one of the most pleasant smelling of mushrooms and versatile for cooking. It is mostly used for soups. A recommended cooking method is to cut up the small caps, sauté in fat so they release their aromatic juices and then use in soup. Always be careful when picking to observe where it grows, so as not to mistake it for galerinas. The Changeable Agaric/Pholiota usually grows on the wood remains of deciduous trees and must have a scaly stem and a very pleasant, fruity mushroom smell and taste.

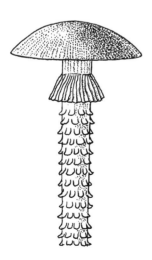

The Changeable Agaric/Pholiota has a scaly stem, pleasant smell and taste.

147

☠ **Marginate Galerina**

Galerina marginata (Batsch ex Fr.) Sing.

The cap is 15 to 50 mm wide, soon becoming bell-shaped, later flat, smooth, grooved at the margin, darkening when moist, yellow-brown, light ochre-brown when dry. The skin is slightly viscid when moist. The gills are adnate at the stem, cinnamon-brown to rusty-brown, 4 to 6 mm high. The stem is cylindrical, 40 to 100 mm long, 5 to 7 mm wide, tubed, slightly crooked, with a ring at the top, fibrous, ochre-brown to dark-brown at the base. The ring sometimes disappears leaving only a brown strip. The flesh is thin, brownish, with a floury cucumber smell and taste. It grows from June to October on stumps, branches, sawdust and conifer bark, individually or in small clusters, sometimes abundantly but usually quite sparsely. It contains the same poisonous substances as the Death Cap and, hence, is one of the deadly poisonous species. It could be mistaken when picking the popular Changeable Agaric/Pholiota which normally grows on the wood remains of deciduous trees but may also be found on conifers.

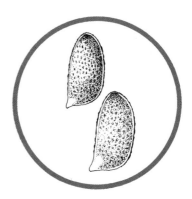

The spores of the Marginate Galerina which grows on conifers.

Changeable Agaric; Changeable Pholiota

Kuehneromyces mutabilis (Schaeff. ex Fr.) Sing. et Smith

The cap measures 20 to 70 mm in diameter, is bell-shaped at first, later low arched, finally flat with a low knob, smooth, naked, very hygrophanous (rusty dark-brown in damp weather, viscid, fading to light honey-brown when dry). The mushroom easily soaks up water and fruit bodies can be found in the rain. The caps have a two-coloured surface – a yellowish centre with a darker border. The cap colour fades when dry but always from the apex towards the margin. The gills are covered when young with a membrane which later changes into a ring. At first they are light-ochre, later cinnamon-brown to rusty-brown, adnexed at the stem. The stem is cylindrical, slightly folded, 40 to 100 mm long, tubed, with roots and interwoven with the surrounding Changeable Agarics/Pholiotas, pale at the top, finely grooved with tiny scales under the ring, brown to black-brown at the base. The flesh is whitish, slightly brownish, with a very pleasant fruity mushroom smell and taste. It grows from early spring to winter, usually from remains of deciduous trees (birches, lindens etc.). It often appears after rain, grow-ing on stumps in rich clusters. Check to see whether the mushroom grows from a deciduous tree so it is not mistaken for the Marginate Galerina. Another guideline, though less reliable, is the smell of the Changeable Agaric/ Pholiota and the scaly stem.

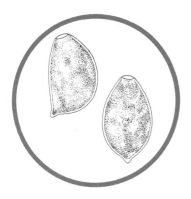

The spores of the Changeable Agaric/Pholiota which can best be recognised by the fact that it usually grows from the remains of deciduous trees.

☠ **White Tricholoma**

Tricholoma album (Schaeff. ex Fr.) Kumm.

The cap is 40 to 120 mm wide, almost convex when young, soon becoming broadly arched, often with a rounded knob, with a well inrolled margin, white or pale ochre-yellowish or with a fleshy tinge and a brownish centre. The skin is smooth, soon becoming dry, shiny; light, whitish colour tones predominate when it is dry. The gills are dense, thick, sinuate and decurrent at the stem, firm, creamy-yellowish with age. The stem is whitish, finely grained at the top, cylindrical, usually bent at the bottom. The flesh is white, unpleasant, and has a bitter burning taste. The unpleasant bug-like smell changes with age into a disgusting coal gas stink. It grows from August to October in deciduous woodlands, mostly under birches and beeches from lowlands to highlands. For example it can be found growing in masses in forests where there is a greater occurrence of birches, but is quite a rare sight in other kinds of woodland. It is a moderately poisonous mushroom causing diarrhoea and vomiting.

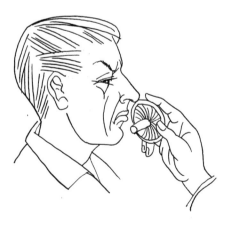

The White Tricholoma has a burning taste and a disgusting smell.

Tricholomataceae

Dove Tricholoma
Tricholoma columbetta (Fr.) Kumm.

The cap measures 50 to 120 mm in diameter, is arched when young with an inrolled margin, later flat with a folded margin; white, with a silky sheen and crimson-coloured patches. The gills are white at first, creamy-yellowish with age, quite high with uneven edges. The stem is white, fibrous, thick, uneven, sometimes bluish at the bottom and usually covered in soil at the base. The flesh is white, juicy, with a pleasant floury smell and delicious mushroom taste. It grows from August to October in light mixed woodlands, mainly under birches, in lowlands and highlands. In some regions it grows in masses under birches, elsewhere it is a rarity. It is an edible and very tasty mushroom thanks to its firm flesh which is suitable for a number of culinary dishes including salads, creamy soups or pie fillings. Be careful when picking the mushroom not to confuse it with the White Tricholoma (which also grows under birches). It is always better to taste the fruit body beforehand. The White Tricholoma is betrayed by its disgusting smell and unpleasant burning taste.

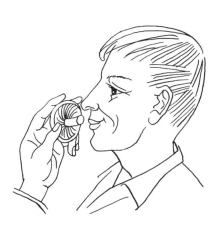

The Dove Tricholoma has a delicious taste and pleasant smell.

☠ **White-Brown Tricholoma**

Tricholoma albobrunneum (Pers. ex Fr.) Kumm.

The cap measures 40 to 90 mm in diameter, is convex at first with an inrolled margin, later broadly arched, curved to folded. The skin has finely ingrowing fibres, is viscid when damp, shiny when dry, red-brown, sometimes grooved at the margin, finely grained in the centre. The gills are rounded, narrowly attached (adnexed) to the stem, white, going brown when pressed or with age, sometimes rusty patches appear in middle age. The stem is cylindrical, white at the top, finely scaly, separated with a marked round strip from the bottom brownish part; the border of the colour transition at the stem is often greatly defined which is typical of the White-Brown Tricholoma. The flesh is white, with a pleasantly floury taste at first then becoming bitter with a floury cucumber smell. It grows sporadically from August to October in coniferous woodlands mostly in mountainous pine woods. It is a moderately poisonous mushroom causing stomach problems and diarrhoea. In view of the fact that brown tricholomas are difficult to determine, it is better to avoid any tricholomas found in coniferous woods. The Sandy/Poplar Tricholoma, which most resembles the White-Brown Tricholoma, should only picked from under poplars and not conifers.

The White-Brown Tricholoma has a clear light-coloured round strip at the top of the stem.

Sandy/Poplar Tricholoma

Tricholoma populinum J. Lange

A detailed description is found on page 133. The Sandy/Poplar Tricholoma grows from August to October under poplars in woodlands, groves, orchards and avenues in lowlands and highlands. It grows on one site for many years, sometimes found in large amounts. It is a very tasty mushroom for cooking, and is used for making sauces, soups etc. It is particularly suitable for pickling. The poisonous White-Brown Tricholoma can be distinguished from this mushroom by the white-brown colour transition on the stem.

Sandy/Poplar Tricholoma

Yellow-Brown Tricholoma

Tricholomataceae

Tricholoma fulvum (D.C. ex Fr.) Sacc.

The cap measures 50 to 120 mm in diameter, when young it is broadly conical with an inrolled margin, later broadly arched with a low rounded knob, fleshy in the middle. It is rather thin at the margin, viscid when moist; brown-rusty, lighter or darker brown; darker in the middle, lighter at the margin, with finely flattened flaky fibres to almost a bald surface; radial wrinkles appear when old at the margin. The gills are quite dense, sinuate at the stem, loosely decurrent, pale yellow at first, later yellow, turning rusty when old with spots on the edges. The stem is cylindrical, up to 20 mm wide, full when young, later hollow, yellowish with lengthwise brownish fibres, dark brown at the base, sticky. The flesh in the cap is usually whitish, yellow in the stem and rusty-brown in the base of the stem. The yellow colour of the flesh is rich sometimes and pale yellow at others; its colour is most intensive at the surface of the stem. The flesh has a floury, slightly radish-like smell and pleasant, indistinctive taste. It grows from August to October in all woodlands particularly in great abundance under birches. The fruit bodies usually appear in clumps in grassy glades, along woodland paths, on woodland borders and outside woods. There are conflicting opinions about whether or not this is an edible mushroom. However, without doubt the Yellow-Brown Tricholoma is responsible for numerous cases of mild poisoning accompanied by diarrhoea and vomiting.

A section of the Yellow-Brown Tricholoma

Sandy/Poplar Tricholoma 🍴

Tricholoma populinum J. Lange

Plums and Custard 🍴

Tricholomopsis rutilans (Schaeff. ex Fr.) Sing.

Sandy/Poplar Tricholoma

A detailed description of the Sandy/Poplar Tricholoma is found on page 133. It is an edible and tasty mushroom and versatile for culinary use. It can be distinguished from the Yellow-Brown Tricholoma by the fact that the flesh under the skin of its stem is not yellow.

Plums and Custard

Plums and Custard is described in detail on page 123. It grows abundantly, both individually and in clusters in the summer and autumn, on old stumps and hidden dead conifer roots. The fruit bodies taste best when young. Plums and Custard can be safely distinguished from the Yellow-Brown Tricholoma by its purple tomentose cap when young and golden-coloured gills and flesh. The Yellow-Brown Tricholoma is mostly found growing under pines.

Sandy/Poplar Tricholoma

Plums and Custard

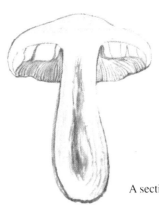

A section of the Sandy/Poplar Tricholoma

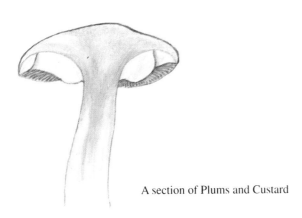

A section of Plums and Custard

155

☠ **Ceruse Clitocybe**

Clitocybe cerussata (Fr.) Kumm.

The cap is 50 to 90 mm wide and slightly arched when young with a blunt knob, later broadly flat to funnel-shaped, smooth, rich white, hoary white, dirty white with age to fair-ochre with concentrated rings of cracked skin. When young it is slightly inrolled, later it has lobed folds and a sharp margin. The gills are 3 to 5 mm high, dense, thin, narrowing off at both ends, slightly decurrent at the stem, white at first, later a dirty-white to light-cream. The stem is cylindrical, a bit thicker at the bottom and white tomentose, 20 to 50 mm high, 3 to 10 mm wide, white, smooth, naked, flexible, full when young and resembles, cotton wool with age. The flesh is white and does not change colour if cut. It is flexible when young, later soft; it has a mellow cabbage-like taste and smell. It grows in the autumn in coniferous and deciduous woods, on damp sites. It can be found in great numbers growing in strips or so-called witches' rings. The mushroom is found throughout the temperate zone of the Northern hemisphere. The Ceruse Clitocybe is classed as a poisonous mushroom for its high content of muscarine. Confusion may occur when picking the Miller/Plum Agaric Sweetbread Mushroom or Fairy-Ring Champignon. The first symptoms after eating a large amount of the poisonous Ceruse Clitocybe appear in about 30 minutes. The victim feels discomfort, anxiety, sweats a lot and has cold shivers. Salivation increases followed by painful stomach cramps. The patient feels marked muscular weakness, has blurred vision and loses a lot of liquid. Medical treatment is required.

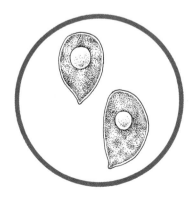

The Ceruse Clitocybe has ellipsoid, smooth colourless spores.

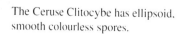

Miller; Plum Agaric; Sweetbread Mushroom

Clitopilus prunulus (Scop. ex Fr.) Kumm.

The cap measures 30 to 100 mm in diameter, is convex at first, later becoming arched even slightly depressed, a bit curved with a long in-rolled finely hoary margin, white or slightly sweetish, smooth, matt and dry. The gills are dense, low, long and decurrent, whitish at first, fleshy pink with age. The stem is short, cylindrical, sometimes strange looking, full, white and tough. The flesh is white, with a floury cucumber taste and strong floury smell. It grows from June to October in all kinds of woods, on their borders, in woodland meadows and everywhere where white boletes are found. It is one of the good edible mushrooms. It can be distinguished from the Ceruse Clitocybe by its long decurrent gills which are fleshy pink when older and by the spores which have distinctive ridges.

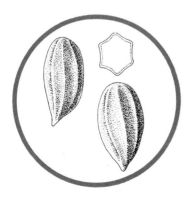

The Miller/Plum Agaric/Sweetbread Mushroom has fusiform, pink-coloured spores with six lengthwise ridges.

157

☠ **Whitish Bolete**

Boletus albidus Roques

The cap measures 50 to 200 mm in diameter, is convex when young, later flat, well inrolled at the margin, greyish, whitish or grey-ochre, finely hoary with a silky sheen, often pitted; if pressed then it goes grey-blue. The tubes are 15 to 30 mm long, pale-yellow at first, later lemon-yellow, ochre-yellow with age; they turn blue when cut. They are sinuate at the stem. The mouth of the tubes is ochre to ochre-brown, but turning blue when pressed. The stem is barrel-shaped when young, club-shaped to cylindrical when older, often with roots at the base, light-yellow with a network at the top, light-ochre in other parts, sometimes with red patches. The flesh is yellowish, only slightly blue, tasty, solid, with an unpleasant carbolic acid-like smell and bitter taste. It grows quite rarely from July to October on warmer sites in deciduous woodlands, groves and the banks of ponds under oaks. It is a mildly poisonous mushroom causing stomach problems in some people. The unpleasant taste remains after cooking, so it is unsuitable for consumption.

The flesh of the Whitish Bolete, on a cross-section of the fruit body, goes slightly blue and has a strong carbolic acid-like smell.

Butter Bolete

Boletus appendiculatus Schaeff. ex Fr.

The cap is 70 to 200 mm wide, convex when young with an inrolled margin, later arched, cushion-like with age with a sharp margin and finely ingrowing fibres; yellow-brown at first, later darker to red-brown, going rusty-brown when pressed. The tubes are pale yellow, turning olive-green-yellow with age. The mouth of the tubes is orbicular when young, golden-yellow, and golden-brown when older, and a slight blue-green colour when pressed. The stem is like a thick beetroot when young, later cylindrical with a conically elongated base, golden-yellow, ochre-brown at the bottom, decorated on the upper part with a fine yellow network which later disappears. The flesh is yellow, a bit brownish at the base of the stem, less commonly with a reddish tinge, turning a pale blue above the tubes when cut; quite tough though softening later; has a delicious sweet mushroom taste and fine, indistinctive smell. It grows from July to September in warm deciduous woodlands, mainly under edible mushrooms. The Butter Bolete cannot be confused with the Whitish Bolete as the former does not have a greyish cap and is not bitter.

The flesh of the Butter Bolete is white (it turns a pale blue colour only above the tubes) and has a pleasant taste and smell.

☠ Strong-Scented Agaric; Soapy Tricholoma

Tricholoma saponaceum (Fr.) Kumm.

The cap is 50 to 100 mm wide, convex when young or bell-shaped with a knob in the centre, later flat with irregular folds, whitish, greyish, greenish, olive or reddish to red-brown, smooth, naked, shiny, viscid when moist, with shelf-like cracks when dry. The gills are sparse, sinuate and narrowly attached to the stem; thick, whitish (with shades of green); the older gills are greyish to yellowish, reddening in places, curved, serrated at the edges. The stem is variable, cylindrical, erect or crooked, uneven, swollen, with roots at the bottom, smooth, finely fibrous, with red-brown scales or covered with dark dust, white, going grey, rusty to red with age. The flesh is white, turning pink slowly when cut or injured, with an unpleasant, repulsive taste (resembling lye) and soapy smell. It grows abundantly from July to November in all woods in lowlands and mountains. It appears in big clumps in coniferous woodlands. It is moderately poisonous causing digestive problems such as vomiting and diarrhoea. Symptoms indicate the presence of muscarine. The Strong-Scented Agaric/Soapy Tricholoma is sometimes mistaken by mushroom pickers for the Sandy/Poplar Tricholoma, the Firwood Agaric/Man On Horseback or the Dingy Agaric/Streaked Tricholoma.

A cross-section of the fruit body of the Strong-Scented Agaric/Soapy Tricholoma

Sandy/Poplar Tricholoma 🍴
Tricholoma populinum J. Lange

Firwood Agaric; Man On Horseback 🍴
Tricholoma flavovirens (Pers. ex Fr.) Lund.

Dingy Agaric; Streaked Tricholoma 🍴
Tricholoma portentosum (Fr.) Quél.

Sandy/Poplar Tricholoma
A detailed description is found on page 133.

Firwood Agaric; Man On Horseback
A detailed description is found on page 113.

Dingy Agaric; Streaked Tricholoma
A detailed description is found on page 109.
All three edible Tricholomas are tasty and versatile cooking mushrooms. They have a pleasant floury smell (unlike the Strong-Scented Agaric/Soapy Tricholoma) and do not turn pink or red when injured. The Firwood Agaric/Man On Horseback and the Dingy Agaric/Streaked Tricholoma have a nutty taste. Moreover the Firwood Agaric/Man On Horseback differs from the Strong/Scented Agaric/Soapy Tricholoma in its bright yellow gills.

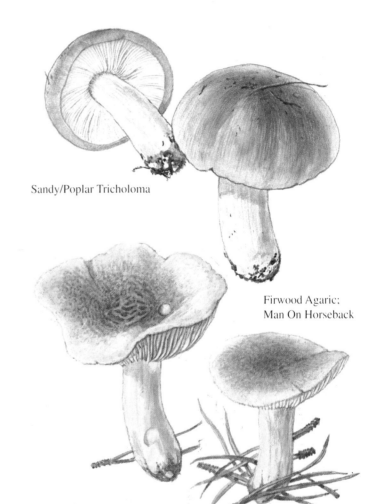

Sandy/Poplar Tricholoma

Firwood Agaric;
Man On Horseback

A cross-section of the Firwood Agaric/Man On Horseback

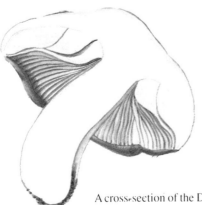

A cross-section of the Dingy Agaric/Streaked Tricholoma

Dingy Agaric;
Streaked Tricholoma

☠ Booted Amanita

Amanita porphyria (Alb. et Schw. ex Fr.) Sacc.

The cap measures 40 to 80 mm in diameter, is convex at first, soon becoming bell-shaped, later arched to flat, grey-violet to brown-grey, ungrooved at the margin, thin-fleshed, usually naked with several large light grey-violet scabs when dry which are the remains of the veil. When dry the skin of the cap is shiny and dry. The gills are free at the stem, dense, white, sometimes yellowish with age. The stem can be easily broken off, is cylindrical, slender, whitish with a grey-violet tinge, it resembles cotton wool at first and later forms hollow tubes; terminates in a large soft, grey-violet bulb which is sharply cut off at the upper part. Sometimes a grey-violet volva, with a low somewhat ragged border, is found growing around the bulb. When young gills are covered in a membranous white to grey-violet veil which changes in old age into a lank, grooved grey-violet ring attached to the stem. The flesh is white, firm, greyish under the skin of the cap, and has a potato or mild radish-like taste and smells like raw potatoes. It grows sporadically from July to October in coniferous woodlands with acid soil. On rare occasions it can be found growing under oaks. It is most common in mountainous regions. In view of the buphotenine and indole content, it is moderately poisonous. When picked it can be mistaken for any of the edible amanitas.

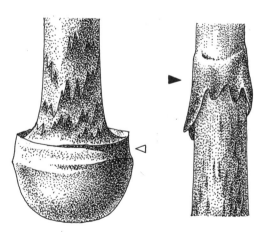

The Booted Amanita has a ring on its stem when older; the stems terminate in a sharp cut off bulb.

Gilded Amanita

Amanita inaurata Secr.

The cap measures 100 to 150 mm in diameter, is umber-brown in colour covered with large grey-brown scabs, i.e. remains of the veil which had previously covered the entire fruit body. At first the cap is egg-shaped and enveloped in a greyish to whitish case, later becoming shaped like a rounded arch. The remains of the veil in the form of scabs remain on the skin of the cap therefore clearly distinguishing the Gilded Amanita from similar species. The gills are dense, high, white and free at the stem. The stem is up to 180 mm high, whitish, covered with conspicuous scaly cracks, breakable, broadening out gradually at the bottom, covered at the base with a pointed volva which is light on the outside and umber-covered inside. The flesh is whitish, watery, very fragile, and has a sweetish taste and indistinctive smell. It grows rarely from July to October in coniferous woodlands. It is an edible though not very tasty mushroom. It can be easily distinguished from the Booted Amanita because it has no ring and the bottom part of the stem is usually enveloped in a high, loose, pointed volva.

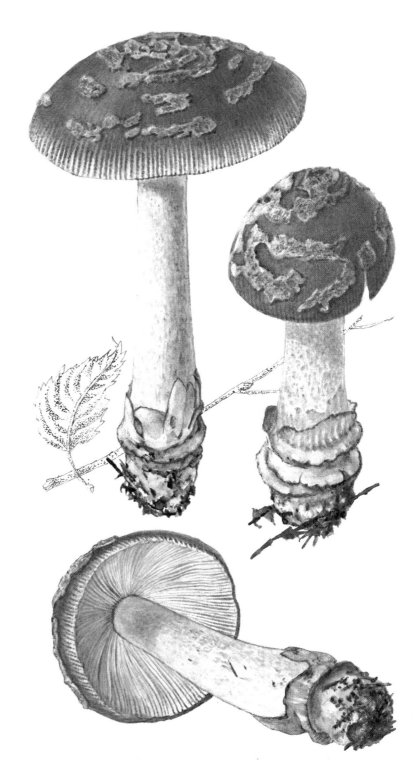

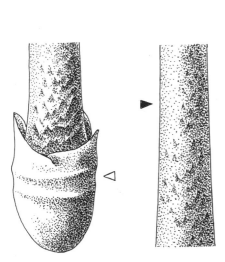

The Gilded Amanita has no ring; the stem broadens out into a bulb enveloped, at the bottom, in a high loose volva.

☠ Poisonous Amanita

Amanita virosa (Fr.) Bertillon

The cap is 40 to 100 mm wide, shaped like a long cone, arched to flat with age. The skin is viscid at first, soon becoming dry, smooth with a silky sheen, white, sometimes yellowish at the centre of the cap. The gills are covered in a white membranous veil in youth which changes in old age into a white smooth lank ring. The gills are dense, remain pure white, and are free and finely fringed at the edges. The stem is coarsely scaled, thinnest at the top, broadens out at the bottom and terminates in a robust, soft spherical bulb; it grows from a high, loose, conspicuously pointed white volva. The flesh remains pure white. When old the flesh has a sweetish smell resembling raw potatoes. It grows sporadically from July to October in coniferous woodlands, in lowlands under pine trees and under spruce trees on higher ground. In some places it is not found at all. It is a deadly poisonous mushroom causing liver damage, like the Death Cap.

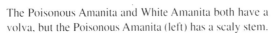

The Poisonous Amanita and White Amanita both have a volva, but the Poisonous Amanita (left) has a scaly stem.

White Amanita

Amanita alba Gill.

Snow-White Agaricus

Agaricus chionodermus Pilát

White Amanita

The fruit body is white all over, it differs from the Poisonous Amanita mainly because it has no ring in adulthood. The cap is 40 to 100 mm wide, bell-shaped after the white case is torn, finally broadly flat, white with short grooves at the margin, shiny when dry. The gills are arched, dense and white. The stem is cylindrical, becomes hollow, white and growing from a white membranous volva. The flesh is white, juicy, with a pleasant mushroom smell and taste. It grows from June to October in grassy woodlands mostly under birches. The White Amanita is an edible mushroom.

Snow-White Agaricus

This relatively rare champignon mushroom considerably resembles the Horse Mushroom, but is always pure white in colour without the slight yellowish tinge. The cap is covered with indistinctive, fine, attached, rather large white scales which almost disappear when the cap dries up in old age. The gills are white at first, soon becoming a rich pink colour. The flesh goes yellow only at the bottom of the stem after a long while. It has a pleasant smell. It grows from May to autumn in flooded meadows of deciduous groves or in spruce woods on limestone ground. It is an edible mushroom. The Snow-White Agaricus differs from the Poisonous Amanita in the pink colour of its gills and it does not have a volva.

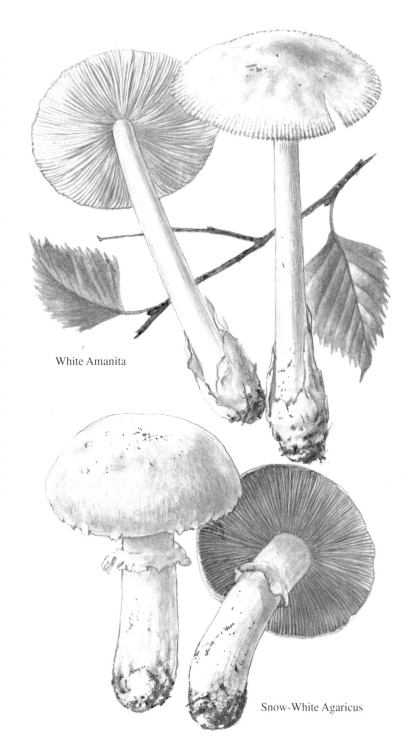

White Amanita

Snow-White Agaricus

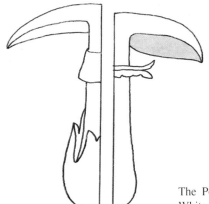

The Poisonous Amanita (left) differs from the Snow-White Agaricus (right) in the colour of its gills and volva.

165

☠ Broad-Gill

Megacollybia platyphylla (Pers. ex Fr.) Kotl. et Pouz.

The cap is 50 to 200 mm wide, convex at first, later arched to flat and slightly depressed; greyish-ash or grey-brown in colour; smooth, with radial cracks when old. The gills are white, sparse, paunchy, 30 mm high, yellowish-brown when old, cut off to almost loosely attached at the stem. The stem is cylindrical, lengthwise grooved, resembling cotton wool at first, later hollow, with a club-shaped, whitish base, later pale to yellow-brown, hoary and going bald. Long and branched white mycelial cords grow from the base of the stem which enter the decomposed substrate. The flesh is white, watery, with a tough consistency, fibrous inside the stem, has an indistinctive taste and smell, It grows from June to October on the rotting trunks and stumps of coniferous and deciduous trees or next to them from the roots concealed in the ground. It is mostly found in highland areas. The mushroom may cause digestive problems.

Long mycelial cords grow from the stem of the Broad-Gill.

Beech Rooter 🍴

Oudemansiella radicata (Relh. ex Fr.) Sing.

Deer Mushroom; Fawn Mushroom 🍴

Pluteus atricapillus (Schaeff. ex Fr.) Kumm.

Beech Rooter

The cap measures 40 to 80 mm in diameter, is yellow-brown or grey-brown to brown in colour; distinctly viscid and shiny, particularly sticky when moist, with clear radial wrinkles; bell-shaped at first, soon becoming arched to flat, with a blunt knob in the centre, thin-fleshed and an easy-to-peel skin. The gills are sparse, quite high, paunchy, free and whitish in colour. The stem is cylindrical, slender, tough, naked, with lengthwise grooves, whitish, brownish and thick at the bottom, growing from very long roots reaching down into the substrate. The flesh is white, with an indistinctive taste and smell. It grows from June to October in deciduous woodlands. It is a very tasty mushroom, but only the little caps are picked. It differs from the Broad-Gill in the distinctively viscid surface of its cap and long-rooting stem.

Deer Mushroom; Fawn Mushroom

The cap grows 50 to 100 mm in size, is bell-shaped at first, later convex, finally horizontally flat, grey or grey-brown, shiny, cracked when dry. The gills are very dense, high, free of the stem, whitish at first, later pink. The stem is cylindrical, full, whitish, with dark lengthwise strips, breakable. The flesh is whitish, watery, fragile, with a mellow potato taste. It is commonly found growing from May to November on rotting deciduous tree-trunks and stumps. It is an edible mushroom but rather bland. It differs in its dense pink gills from the Broad-Gill.

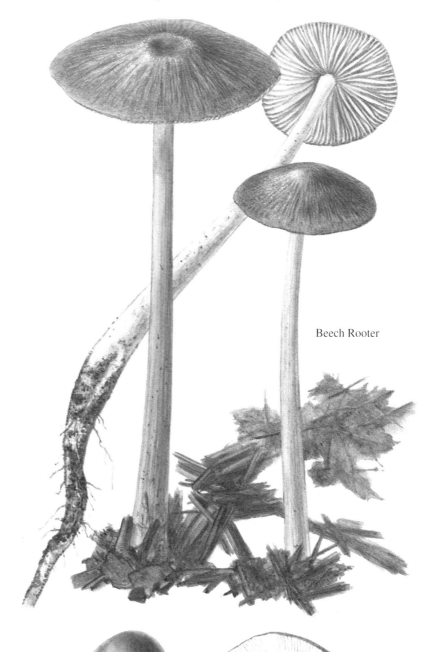

Beech Rooter

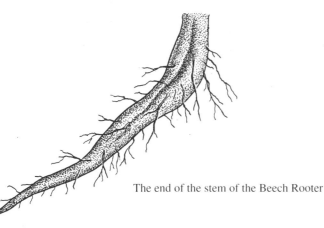

The end of the stem of the Beech Rooter

Deer Mushrom; Fawn Mushroom

167

☠ Russet-Scaly Tricholoma

Tricholomataceae

Tricholoma vaccinum (Pers. ex Fr.) Kumm.

The cap measures 30 to 80 mm in diameter, is conically bell-shaped at first, later flat with a prominent knob; thin-fleshed, covered all over the surface in fibrous raised scales, with a long inrolled margin; has rusty-coloured shaggy hairs, red-brown or red-rusty. The gills are sparse, high, sinuate at the stem, dirty-white at first, later with reddish and brownish specks. The stem is cylindrical, a bit paunchy at the bottom, usually hollow, quite short, red-brown, whitish and flaky under the cap, otherwise fibrous and scaly. At first the margin of the cap is joined to the stem by a fibrous veil which soon disappears. The flesh is whitish, later a bit rusty, with an earthy smell and bitter to unpleasant bitter-sour taste. It grows from July to October in coniferous woodlands, mostly among younger spruces. It is one of the most common of the central European Tricholomas, found on limestone ground in large clumps. However, it is unsuitable for cooking, causing digestive problems such as diarrhoea and vomiting.

A cross-section of the Russet-Scaly Tricholoma

Tricholoma Imbricatum

Tricholoma imbricatum (Fr. ex Fr.) Kumm.

The cap measures 40 to 100 mm diameter. At first it is bluntly conical, later flat with a low knob, thin-fleshed, red-brown to light chestnut brown; when young smooth and downy or almost completely smooth, later covered with fine fibrous scales with a bald apex and margin; always dry, tucked under at the margin at first, later with a sharp margin. The gills are quite dense, high, whitish at first, turning brown when pressed, sharply uneven at the edges, and rounded at the stem. The stem is cylindrical, firm, full, whitish on top, otherwise with red-brown fibres and without a veil. The flesh is white, brownish in the stem, with an indistinctive smell and taste; sometimes it is slightly bitter. It grows, but not abundantly, from August to October in coniferous woodlands particularly in young grassy pine woods on sandy soil; it is there that it grows in large dense clumps. It is a versatile mushroom for cooking, particularly suitable for recipes containing other species. It differs from the Russet-Scaly Tricholoma because its cap only has fine fibrous scales, tucked under when young (but not inrolled), and the stem has no veil. The place where it grows is also different as the Russet-Scaly Tricholoma seeks out sites in young damp spruce woods.

A cross-section of the *Tricholoma imbricatum*

☠ Shingled Tricholoma

Tricholomataceae

Tricholoma pessundatum (Fr.) Quél.

The cap is 60 to 120 mm wide, almost convex at first, later arched to broadly flat, often irregularly folded, red-brown to chestnut-brown, lighter at the margin, smooth, bald, viscid when moist; the margin of the cap is inrolled when young and it evens out later. The gills are quite dense and wide, deeply sinuate to almost free at the stem, white, later light brownish to rusty with red-rusty patches. The stem is 40 to 70 mm long, 15 to 30 mm wide, thickset, often almost bulbous-like when young, later a bit elongated, cylindrical, often crooked and irregular, full, firm, whitish or slightly brownish, flaky, hairy, later balding, dusty hoary at the top. The flesh is compact, fibrous, white, turning a pale red-rusty colour. It has a distinctive smell of fresh flour and also has a strong floury, slightly acid but not a bitter taste. It grows quite sparsely from August to October in spruce and pine woods, usually individually, sometimes in small clumps. It is a moderately poisonous mushroom causing quite persistent digestive problems including vomiting and diarrhoea.

The young fruit body of the Shingled Tricholoma

Sandy/Poplar Tricholoma
Tricholoma populinum J. Lange 🍴

Weasel Russula
Russula mustelina Fr. 🍴

Sandy/Poplar Tricholoma

A detailed description is found on page 133. The Sandy/Poplar Tricholoma grows from August to October under poplars in woods, groves, orchards and avenues in lowlands and highlands. It is easy to distinguish from the Shingled Tricholoma because it never grows in coniferous woodlands.

Weasel Russula

The cap is 50 to 150 mm wide, convex at first, later flat and depressed; a hazelnut to chestnut-brown colour, matt, dry with a difficult-to-peel skin. The gills are dense, white, later creamy with brown specks on the edges. The stem is cylindrical, white and full at first, with rusty specks later and resembling cotton wool. The flesh is white, brownish under the skin of the cap, going a bit rusty in old age, with an indistinctive smell and very pleasant, delicious, nutty taste. It grows from July to October in highland spruce woods, in some places in great numbers, elsewhere it does not occur at all. Thanks to its excellent taste and the firm consistency of the flesh it is a popular mushroom, suitable for being prepared for cooking in various ways. It is easy to distinguish from the Shingled Tricholoma because it does not have gills at the stem which is sinuate; no fibrous flesh can be extracted even if the stem is stabbed.

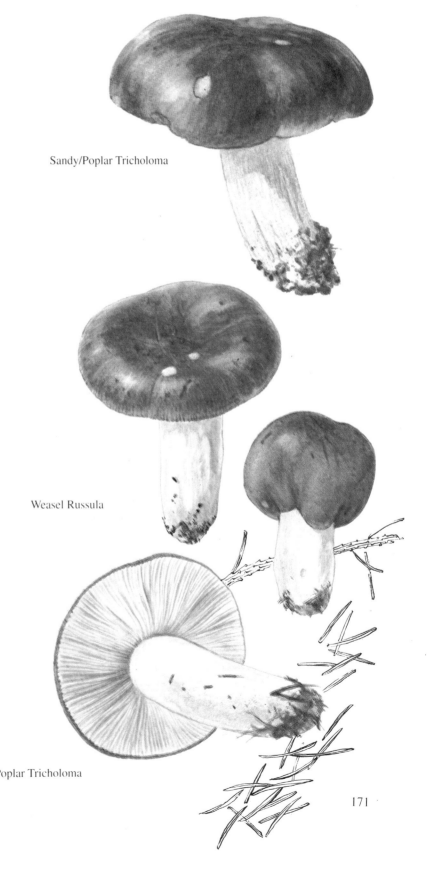

Sandy/Poplar Tricholoma

Weasel Russula

A young fruit body of the Sandy/Poplar Tricholoma

Liberty Cap

Psilocybe semilanceata (Fr.) Kumm.

The cap is 15 mm high and 5 to 9 mm wide, olive-grey-brown, yellow-brown or greenish-yellow, permanently conical, always with a prominent knob on top, viscid, bald, finely grooved, membranous, with a tucked under margin at the stem. The gills are olive-grey and black-brown when old, moderately dense, high and prominent and lighter at the edges. The stem is very long, in curved folds, unbreakable, thin, light-brown or ochre in colour. The flesh is very thin, fragile, light-ochre, of a slightly radish-like taste and indistinctive smell. It grows rarely from August to October in grass of pastureland, on land boundaries, grassy paths and grassy woodland borders in lowlands and mountains. Large numbers of fruit bodies can be found in such places where growing conditions are favourable; they grow individually and not in clusters. It is a moderately poisonous mushroom. It is one of the hallucinogenic species of mushroom whose effects on people have not been fully tested and verified. Poisoning symptoms after consumption occur in different ways. Some people get a feeling of euphoria, laugh, suffer defective vision accompanied by hallucinations, others feel anxiety, fear, have terrible visions leading to delirium and suicide attempts.

A cross-section of the fruit body of the Liberty Cap

Fairy-Ring Champignon
Marasmius oreades (Bolt. ex Fr.) Fr.

Leathery Mycena
Mycena galericulata (Scop. ex Fr.) S.F. Gray

Fairy-Ring Champignon
A detailed description is found on pages 33 and 73. The Fairy-Ring Champignon grows from May to October on grassy sites, on boundaries and in gardens in highlands and mountains. It is an excellent edible mushroom, good for soups. Only the caps are picked. It can be distinguished from the Liberty Cap because it has sparse gills, a flexible stem and the flesh has a bitter almond smell.

Leathery Mycena
The cap is conical or bell-shaped at first, later arched or broadly flat, 15 to 40 mm wide, grey-white or grey-brown, darker at the centre, radially wrinkled and thin-fleshed. The gills are sparse, decurrent at the stem, whitish at first, later pinkish. The stem is cylindrical, thin, naked, smooth, viscid, grey-yellow, lighter at the top often with long roots. The flesh is watery, grey-ish, with a floury cucumber taste and smell. It grows abundantly from May to November on stumps and in deciduous tree roots hidden in the ground. It grows individually but more often in clusters. It is a good edible mushroom and versatile for cooking. Only the caps are picked. It is easy to distinguish from the Liberty Cap because it has a tough stem and grows on wood.

Fairy-Ring Champignon

Leathery Mycena

A cross-section of the Fairy-Ring Champignon

☠ Leafy Clitocybe

Clitocybe phyllophila (Fr.) Kumm.

The cap measures 40 to 60 mm in diameter, is low arched when young, later flat and broad, with a shallow depression; hoary-white at first, balding, white when dry and watery-brown when moist with transparent gills at the margin. The gills are dense, low, shortly decurrent at the stem, white at first, yellowish with age. The stem is thin, flexible, usually creased, hollow, with a felt cover at the bottom, white to watery-brown with white fibres. The flesh is thin, whitish, with a mellow fruity and aniseed-like smell and pleasant, mild taste. It grows from August to October in deciduous, coniferous and mixed woodlands. It grows in clumps forming entire rings or strips. It is quite common in drier and warmer regions together with other whitish clitocybe mushrooms. As yet the systematic classification of white clitocybe mushrooms has not been defined and individual species are still the subject of study. For example during the study of pure cultures it was shown that Pine-Needle Clitocybe (*Clitocybe pythiophila*) is identical with the Leafy Clitocybe. The Leafy Clitocybe is one of the strongly poisonous whitish Clitocybes with a relatively high content of muscarine and may cause the same sort of poisoning as the Sweat-Producing Clitocybe or Ceruse Clitocybe (the course of the poisoning is described on page 156). It may be mistaken for the Miller/Plum Agaric/Sweetbread Mushroom. In view of the difficulty in distinguishing the lighter clitocybe mushrooms by eye, it is better not to pick them at all.

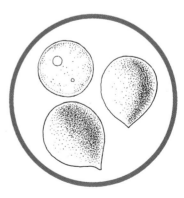

The Leafy Clitocybe has smooth colourless egg-shaped spores.

Miller; Plum Agaric; Sweetbread Mushroom

Clitopilus prunulus (Scop. ex Fr.) Kumm.

A detailed description is found on page 157. The Miller/Plum Agaric/Sweetbread Mushroom grows from June to October in all kinds of wood, on their borders and in woodland meadows. It is one of the good edible mushrooms, but there is a danger that it can be confused with one of the white Clitocybe species. The gills of the Miller/Plum Agaric/Sweetbread Mushroom and the light Clitocybes may have similar colouring and smell alike. Only a good mushroom picker can recognise the Miller/ Plum Agaric/Sweetbread Mushroom by its cucumber taste. The Miller/Plum Agaric/ Sweetbread Mushroom can be reliably distinguished from the Leafy Clitocybe by the spores: the spores of the Leafy Clitocybe are smooth, egg-shaped and colourless whereas those of the Miller/Plum Agaric/Sweetbread Mushroom are pink, fusiform with marked lengthwise ridges.

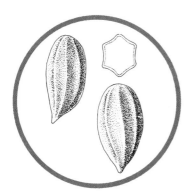

The Miller/Plum Agaric/Sweetbread Mushroom has pink, fusiform spores with lengthwise ridges.

☠ # Sweat-Producing Clitocybe

Tricholomataceae

Clitocybe dealbata (Sow. ex Fr.) Kumm.

The cap is 25 to 40 mm wide, low arched at first with a long inrolled margin, later becoming broadly flat with a shallow depression; viscid when moist, shiny when dry, silky, hoary-looking when young; white to pale yellow or greyish, cracked when old. The gills are dense, shortly decurrent, dirty-white, more decurrent at the stem when old. The stem is cylindrical, short, thin, erect, rounded or creased, fibrous, full, whitish, greyish to pinkish with age. The flesh is thin, white, pinkish inside the stem, the smell resembles fresh wood and has a mellow sweet to dull taste. It grows from August to October in meadow grass, in light woods, on pastures, grassy paths, in parks, gardens, rubbish heaps and sandy steppe-like formations in warmer regions. It is one of the highly poisonous mushrooms with a high muscarine content. It may be confused with the Miller/Plum Agaric/Sweetbread Mushroom or the Fairy-Ring Champignon – a fatal mistake. The course of the poisoning is described under the related Ceruse Clitocybe on page 156. However the Sweat-Producing Clitocybe has a higher muscarine content and is therefore more dangerous.

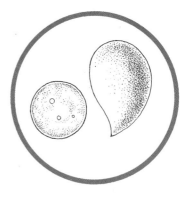

The Sweat-Producing Clitocybe has egg-shaped, short, smooth colourless spores reaching 4.5 to 6 x 2.5 to 4 µm in size.

Miller; Plum Agaric; Sweetbread Mushroom

Clitopilus prunulus (Scop. ex Fr.) Kumm.

A detailed description is found on page 157. The Miller/Plum Agaric/Sweetbread Mushroom grows in lowlands and mountains everywhere where white boletes are found. So according to weather-lore and experienced mushroom pickers, where there is Miller/Plum Agaric/Sweetbread Mushroom, a bolete mushroom can be found growing nearby. It is sometimes quite difficult to distinguish the Miller/Plum Agaric/Sweetbread Mushroom from the Sweat-Producing Clitocybe and requires longer practice in picking. The most reliable way to distinguish one from the other is by the microscopic identification of the spores: those of the Miller/Plum Agaric/Sweetbread Mushroom are pink, fusiform with lengthwise ridges whereas those of the Sweat-Producing Clitocybe are egg-shaped, short, smooth and colourless.

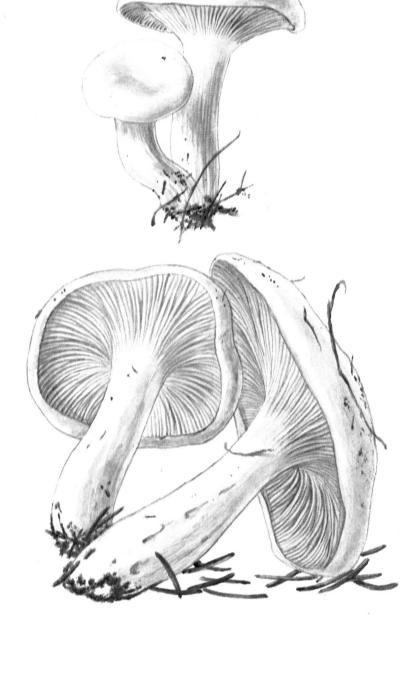

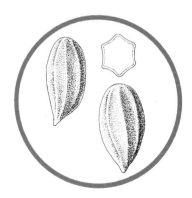

The Miller/Plum Agaric/Sweetbread Mushroom has fusiform spores with six pink-coloured lengthwise ridges.

☠ Honey Fungus

Armillaria mellea (Vahl. ex Fr.) Kumm.

The cap measures 30 to 110 mm in diameter, is convex when young, later arched with a knob, becoming flat and broad; light honey-yellow, yellow-ochre, yellow-green or rusty-brown to brown, covered with darker, at first erect, later flattened scales. The gills are moderately dense, thin, decurrent to a point at the stem, white at first, later yellowish or ochre, with darkening specks, covered in white spore dust when old. The stem is cylindrical, even or crooked, long, tough, yellowish or brownish, smooth or finely fibrously striped to flaky, cotton wool-like inside. When young it is joined to the margin of the cap by a whitish, tufty veil which later disappears leaving only a whitish ring. The flesh is whitish, constant, soft inside the cap, fibrous in the stem, with a dull, mellow mushroom smell and an unpleasant, acrid taste. It is found growing abundantly in clusters from August to October on dead and live deciduous and coniferous tree-trunks, stumps, roots and on saplings. It is one of the moderately poisonous or conditioned edible mushrooms. If not cooked properly or in the raw state, it may cause milder poisoning leading to stomach problems, diarrhoea and vomiting. It can be pickled in vinegar by mushroom pickers or added to goulash and soups, but it does require cooking for at least 20 minutes before use.

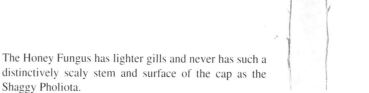

The Honey Fungus has lighter gills and never has such a distinctively scaly stem and surface of the cap as the Shaggy Pholiota.

Shaggy Pholiota

Pholiota squarrosa (Pers. ex Fr.) Kumm.

The cap measures 30 to 100 mm in diameter, is convex at first with an inrolled margin, later broadly flat, is a lemon to ochre-yellow colour, covered with upturned rusty-brown scales, dry. The gills are quite dense, thin, slightly sinuate at the stem and decurrent, olive-yellow, later yellow-brown, in old age rusty-brown. In youth the gills are covered with a membranous yellowish scaly veil which gradually turns into a lemon-yellow or rusty ring. The stem is cylindrical, tough, dry, yellowish with brownish scales. The flesh is yellowish and rusty at the base of the stem, has a repulsive acrid taste and a mellow earthy smell. It grows from August to October in dense clusters usually at the base of dying deciduous trees and sometimes coniferous trees. It prefers deciduous ones. It is a good edible mushroom but only the young fruit bodies are picked. It is easy to distinguish from the Honey Fungus by its dark-coloured spore dust and prominent spores.

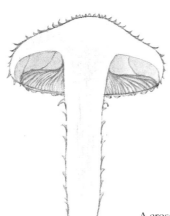

A cross-section of the fruit body of the Shaggy Pholiota

179

☠ Psilocybe Mairei

Psilocybe mairei Sing.

The cap measures 20 to 30 mm in diameter, is broadly conical at first, later flatter with a conically blunt knob, an ochre, light-brown or greyish colour with an olive tinge, strongly hygrophanous, grey-brown when dry, with a blue-green tinge in older creased fruit bodies, bald, moist or a bit viscid with skin which cannot be peeled; sometimes there are membranous whitish remains left on the cap of the veil with the transparent gills. The gills are a dirty grey to ochre colour, becoming rusty after the ripening of the spores, high, narrowly attached (annexed) at the stem, paunchy and rounded, turning blue-green after being injured. The stem has hollow tubes, usually crooked in curves, at the base normally attached to the substrate by a mycelium, whitish to·brownish or a dirty white, with a silky sheen; when old a dirty green-blue colour on the lower part, finely hoary on the upper. The flesh in the cap is very thin, yellowish, pale grey-blue, with a radish taste and dull floury smell. It grows from October to December from woody remains under alders, willows and hornbeams, mostly in the area around brooks or other permanently damp sites. It also grows from the remains of conifers or processed wood. In cooler valleys it is found in masses, otherwise it is a rarity. It is a moderately poisonous mushroom containing psilocin, which has hallucinogenic effects. The victim may suffer from anxiety and fear with terrible visions leading to delirium and suicide attempts.

A cross-section of the fruit body of the *Psilocybe mairei*

Conifer Tuft

Hypholoma capnoides (Fr. ex Fr.) Kumm.

Fairy-Ring Champignon

Marasmius oreades (Bolt. ex Fr.) Fr.

Conifer Tuft

A detailed description is found on page 79. The Conifer Tuft grows abundantly in the autumn in whole clusters in coniferous woodlands from stumps and dead roots, in lowlands and high in the mountains (it can also be seen growing sporadically in the spring). It is a good edible mushroom, suitable, above all, for soups and sauces. It can be distinguished from the *Psilocybe mairei* because the older or creased fruit bodies have no blue-green spots.

Fairy-Ring Champignon

The Fairy-Ring Champignon has been described in detail on pages 33 and 73. It grows from May to October on grassy sites in woodlands, in gardens and on boundaries. It is an excellent edible mushroom, suitable for soups (only the caps are picked). It can be easily distinguished from the *Psilocybe mairei* by its flexible and unbreakable stem, its sparse gills, colouring (the Fairy-Ring Champignon never has any blue-green spots) and never grows on wood.

Conifer Tuft

A cross-section of the Conifer Tuft

A cross-section of the Fairy-Ring Champignon

Fairy-Ring Champignon

Index of common names